The TIO PEPE Guide to the SEAFOOD of SPAIN and PORTUGAL

ALAN DAVIDSON

Originally published by
Gonzalez Byass S.A.
Jerez, Spain

© Alan Davidson 1992, 2002

This edition is published by:
Ediciones Santana, S.L.,
Apartado 422, Fuengirola 29640 (Málaga), Spain
Tel: 952 485 838.   Fax: 952 485 367.
E-mail: info@santanabooks.com
www.santanabooks.com

Cover design by Tina Bradley

Printed by Gráficas San Pancracio, S.L.,
Polígono Industrial San Luis, Calle Orotava 17, Málaga, Spain.

Depósito Legal: MA-572/2002
ISBN 84-89954-21-6

PREFACE TO THE SANTANA EDITION

This has always been one of my special favourites among the books I have written, and I am delighted to think that, thanks to the initiative of Santana Books in publishing a commercial edition, it will now reach a wider audience.

This publication has been made possible by the permission graciously given to me and Santana Books by Gonzalez Byass, with the warm and welcome encouragement of my original sponsor Mauricio Gonzalez-Gordon, Marques de Bonanza.

I take the opportunity to thank Ken Brown and all concerned at Santana Books for the speed and care with which they have produced the new edition. And I express the hope that all new readers will find it as useful as I always intended it to be.

Alan Davidson,
Chelsea, London,
February 2002

ACKNOWLEDGEMENTS

For help in the enjoyable task of writing this book I express thanks to the authors of the works listed in the bibliography; and also to: Miren Aramburu, Asun Balzola, Elizabeth Carter, Roberto Lotina, Jaime Mejuto, Isidoro and Tina Millan, Eulalia Pensado, Alicia Rios, Edite Vieira. At one remove, so to speak, it is fitting that I should repeat thanks already expressed in *Mediterranean Seafood* and *North Atlantic Seafood* to the numerous people in Spain and Portugal who helped me gather information for those books, and to the FAO, whose activities in the last quarter of a century have done so much to illuminate the entire subject of seafood and fisheries throughout the world. But my principal acknowledgement on this occasion must be to Don Mauricio himself, who not only had the idea but also devoted much time and thought to equipping me with reference material.

Alan Davidson
Chelsea, London
April 1992

CONTENTS

FOREWORD

Two hundred years ago, at the end of the eighteenth century, my great, great grandfather, José Antonio González came to live in the little coastal town of Sanlucar de Barrameda, which lies at the mouth of the Guadalquivir river, on the Atlantic coast of southwest Spain.

He had been an officer at the court of King Carlos III in Madrid, but according to legend had lost favour with the King due to his keen interest in some of his Majesty's female courtiers. José Antonio was therefore sent to manage the salt pan marshes of the Crown near the mouth of the Guadalquivir, the great waterway that has played such an important part in Spain's history.

Having lived hundreds of miles from the sea until then, the abundance of fresh seafood must have been a welcome addition to the family's diet – including succulent local fish such as esturion, camarones, angulas and bocas from the estuary, and acedias, langostinos, almejas and coquinas among the many species from the sea.

José Antonio's youngest son, my great grandfather Mañuel M González, established himself as a sherry shipper in the nearby city of Jerez, founding the company González Byass. Mañuel's closest advisor was his uncle José (Tio Pepe), and it was in his honour that our fine sherry, renowned throughout the world, was named Tio Pepe.

It didn't take long for my great grandfather to notice how well seafood matched his favourite wine. Word spread quickly, and soon visitors from all over the world were savouring the subtle combination of flavours. Today, five generations later, we continue to enjoy and to recommend seafood with Tio Pepe – one of the great wines of the world, and one which we advise to be taken daily, well chilled, with oysters, caviar or salmon.

A good pocket guide to seafood is long overdue – one which includes the names of fish in several languages so readers can easily identify and enjoy what they see in the market, on menus or on the table. Alan Davidson, the expert and author of many wonderful books on the subject, has written such a guide, and one which is certain to aid readers in enjoying the seafood of the Iberian Peninsula.

I raise my glass of Tio Pepe to all those who enjoy the good things of life and, in particular, to Alan with our thanks for having taken on and completed the project so beautifully.

Mauricio González-Gordon
Marques de Bonanza
Jerez, June 1992

The Spanish and the Portuguese take seafood seriously, but they can also be light-hearted about it. This drawing, from the remarkable book *Juicio en el Fondo del Mar o la Singularidad de un Carnaval marinero en Santoña* by Fernando Gomarín Guirado and Juan Haya Martínez (Santander, 1986), shows a carnival participant in the guise of a bonito – only one of many such costumes.

INTRODUCTION

During the last 30 years I have written books, quite lengthy ones, about seafood in the Mediterranean; in the Atlantic; and world-wide. Now, thanks to the imaginative idea of Don Mauricio González-Gordon, I have the opportunity to change focus and style in order to produce this pocket-book which maps in terms of seafood the especially interesting area where the species of the Mediterranean and those of the Atlantic meet. Of course, a Mediterranean species will not stop short of the Strait of Gibraltar, as though halted by an invisible traffic sign; and many Atlantic species penetrate the Mediterranean. But, although there is no dividing line, there is a dividing region, and that is provided by the Iberian Peninsula – the Mediterranean and Atlantic coasts of Spain with the coast of Portugal sandwiched between.

What I have sought to do is to catalogue all the species of edible fish, crustaceans and molluscs which are likely to be found in Iberian markets or on the menu of restaurants there. These are listed with their names in the principal languages of the region: Spanish (Castilian) in pride of place, plus Galician (Gallego), Basque (Eusquera), Catalan; and also English, Portuguese, French and German. One species may have many common names even within one language, but I have tried to keep the name-game within bounds by showing only the 'official' ones or those most frequently used.

Otherwise, I offer information about size and colour which, along with the line drawings, should almost always make identification possible. These drawings come from various sources, listed at the end of the book, but it is appropriate to remark here that by far the most important source is the FAO (Food and Agriculture Organization of the United Nations), to whom especially warm thanks, and compliments on the quality of the work done by their artists, are due.

The existence and high quality of the drawings has enabled me to avoid almost completely, in my descriptions, technical details about numbers of fins and so forth – the fins are there in the drawings, plain to see. And I have eschewed any finicky information, such as scale counts or the arrangement of teeth, which would serve only to confuse the general reader for whom the book is intended. However, I do refer sometimes to, for example, dorsal or ventral fins, which terms are not familiar to all. I therefore provide here a diagrammatic drawing of a fish, showing such principal features of its anatomy. The fish shown is not a real one.

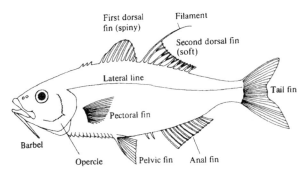

First dorsal fin (spiny) · Filament · Second dorsal fin (soft) · Lateral line · Tail fin · Pectoral fin · Barbel · Opercle · Pelvic fin · Anal fin

A distinction is made in Spain between 'pescado azul', literally blue fish, and others, 'pescado blanco'. The former are what would be called, less romantically, oily or fatty fish in English-speaking countries. Although the distinction is already familiar to people from outside Spain, the emphasis placed on it in Spain is likely to be a surprise. Members of the pescado azul group, such as tuna and mackerel, are named by their colour because, being fish which swim at speed across the surface of deep waters, they mostly have bluish backs and pale undersides, for protection against predators from above or below. And (to put it in overly simple terms) it is they who have oilier flesh because they have to have such strong muscles. But there is, as one would expect, a spectrum of oiliness ranging from over 15% (eg the sardine at certain times of year) down to 1% or less (eg hake and most flatfish), with no exact dividing line – though it seems to be generally agreed that pescado azul are the ones which score over 5%.

The distinction is important to the cook, who needs to know how much oil the fish itself is contributing to the dish; and it is also of considerable interest to nutritionists, since the presence in fish oils of what are called omega-3 fatty acids has emerged in the last two decades as something which is beneficial to us in a number of important ways. Since it is now a common experience to learn that something one has enjoyed eating may be 'bad' for one, it is agreeable to be told that – to take my own case – my long-standing enjoyment of kippers and mackerel and salmon and tuna now counts as a plus in the eyes of nutritionists and doctors.

COOKERY

This is a seafood guide, not a cookbook, so there are no recipes; but the names of well-known seafood dishes are given in the appropriate places, often with brief indications of how these are prepared. Many seafood dishes are not linked to one particular species, but are of wider application. One of the attractive features of seafood for the cook is that alternatives and substitutions and combinations can so readily be adopted. I mention below some of these general recipes.

Almost all countries where seafood is eaten have their special seafood soup/stew dishes; and Spain and Portugal offer some of the finest. The Spanish Bulavesa is the equivalent of the French Bouillabaisse (or, as some would have it, the origin, taken by Catalan fishermen to Marseille in the distant past – see, however, my essay on Bouillabaisse in *A Kipper with My Tea*). Suquet de Peix is a more purely Catalan dish. Sopa de Peix is a Majorcan fish soup. Marmitako, often but not always made with bonito, is a Basque/Cantabrian dish, more than a soup, very good and very hearty.

Zarzuela de Pescado, literally a musical comedy of fish, is a seafood stew popular throughout Spain; usually with squid and prawns in it as well as fish.

In Portugal the most famous fish stew is Caldeirada, of which most versions include potato and onion with the fish and all have plenty of broth (calda). In addition, use of the name fuisado for a fish dish indicates a stew. And, on the soupy side, there are many sorts of Sopa de Peixe, associated with particular regions such as the Algarve and the Alentejo, and all substantial. On the coast of Douro there is another meal-in-itself dish, Sopa de Camarão e Mexilhóes (a chowder of prawns and mussels).

In Spain, the phrases al Gril, a la Parilla, and a la Plancha all mean 'grilled' (broiled). The first refers to grilling with heat from above; the second to grilling over a (for example) charcoal fire; and the last to the other method of grilling, by placing on a hot metal plate.

A Spanish fish dish 'a la Sal' means that the cleaned fish (commonly dorada, but may be lubina, or pargo in Andalucia) has been encased in sea salt and baked thus; see page 59.

Frying is something which Spanish cooks do very willingly, perhaps sometimes to excess. Fried fish dishes are popular in Portugal too, but not quite to the same extent.

Escabeche, a term which has relations in many languages (including the French escabèche and the old English caveach), refers to pickling cooked fish. Thus Agujas en Escabeche consists of pieces of gar-fish which have been fried and then marinated in a 'pickle' of spiced vinegar. Caballas en Escabeche (or Caballas Escabechadas) are mackerel which have been treated in a corresponding way, but without the initial frying.

One unusual and excellent way of cooking such things as clams is to use a cataplana, a special piece of equipment peculiar to the Algarve. It may be made of copper or aluminium, and its shape is best explained by the drawing. It provides a special sort of steamer, tightly sealed when closed, which can be shaken or turned upside down to mix the ingredients.

FRANCE

Sebastian

TRY

R. Ebro

CATALONIA

Barcelona

ARAGON

Tarragona

VALENCIA

Valencia

BALEARIC ISLANDS

MINORCA

Palma

MAJORCA

IBIZA

RCIA

Alicante

MEDITERRANEAN SEA

THE IBERIAN
PENINSULA

A NOTE ON NAMES

Some of the words which appear in names are in parenthesis. This means that the word in question is an optional feature of the name. Thus the Galician name for angler-fish is given as (peixe) sapo; and this indicates that it may be encountered as just 'sapo' or in the longer version 'peixe sapo'. Similarly, gamba (blanca) means that the first word may be used alone, or the full name of two words.

I have given the scientific names of all species which I have listed. This is the only sure way of identifying what one is talking about. For those who are not accustomed to these names, I should explain that they are almost invariably composed of two words, such as *Coryphaena hippurus*, the first indicating the genus and the second the species. Since scientists, for their own good reasons, agree from time to time on changes in this nomenclature, and the superseded names nevertheless remain in currency for a while, I have shown some of the latter and arranged for them to appear also in the index.

ABBREVIATIONS

Gal	Galician (Gallega)
Bas	Basque (Eusquera)
Cat	Catalan
Por	Portuguese
Fre	French
Ger	German
max	maximum
mkt	market
<>	symbol for length
m	male
f	female

HERRING-LIKE FISH

As this catalogue proceeds down the ranks of species of fish, always indicating to which family a species belongs, the most important families will be briefly introduced to the reader.

Certainly the family of herring-like fish must be counted as important. By virtue of the sardine alone it occupies a place of honour in the Iberian Peninsula. It and all its relations share certain characteristics; they have flesh which is rich in oil, and they have numerous small bones.

Although the range of the herring itself does not extend further south than the north of France, and it is not therefore found in Spanish or Portuguese waters, it reaches these countries in conserved from; and it anyway deserves at least a mention here since it is, obviously, the chief member of the important herring family.

The cod and the herring are, historically, the two most important and populous fish of North Atlantic waters, existing in quantities which no fish of warmer waters can rival. So one might think that either or both of them could have become the staple conserved fish in the countries of southern Europe. In fact the cod won this competition easily. The herring has much oilier flesh and cannot be simply salted and dried like cod. Salted and smoked herring have been an export from northern Europe to, for example, Italy in the past; but never on a scale remotely matching the traffic in salt or dried cod.

Family CLUPEIDAE

Clupea harengus

ARENQUE   HERRING

Gal: l	*Por:* arenque
Bas: arrenka	*Fre:* hareng
Cat: arengada	*Ger:* Hering

Since it is absent from Iberian waters, further particulars of fresh herring are not given here, nor is the customary drawing provided.

Sardina pilchardus

SARDINA   SARDINE

Gal: sardiña; xouba,   *Por:* sardinha
parrocha (young)   *Fre:* sardine
Bas: txardiña   *Ger:* Sardine
Cat: sardina, patoya

It is not always realized that what is a sardine when immature becomes a pilchard when fully grown. The market length of *S pilchardus* is 10 cm (sardine size) to 20 cm (pilchard size).

Two slightly larger species of sardine are present in Iberian waters: *Sardinella aurita*, Spanish **alacha**, Portuguese sardinela lombuda; and *Sardinella maderensis*, Spanish **machuelo**, Portuguese sardinela da Madeira. The former of these is distinguished by a pale gold band running back from a gold spot behind the eye; the latter, as the drawing below shows, by a noticeably deeper body.

For many people, sardines come in cans. In Spain and Portugal they are likely to come fresh, and to be grilled: Sardinas Asadas in Spain, Sardinhas Assadas in Portugal. They are often 'butter-flied' (split open and the backbone removed) before being grilled. The particular pleasure (for men) of eating grilled sardines (not just a few but a couple of dozen) in the company of light-hearted women was well described by the Spanish humorist Julio Camba in a memorable essay.

Sardinas en Escabeche, pickled sardines, are available as a home-made delicacy in many restaurants; but in some they will be commercially prepared and from cans.

Larval sardines and anchovies, known as 'aladroch' (the same as 'poutine' in France) have traditionally been cooked, eg in omelettes (Tortilla de Aladroch) in Valencia; but I believe that catching the fish at such a minuscule size is now illegal. They are not to be, although they sometimes are, confused with chanquetes (page 95).

Family CLUPEIDAE
Alosa alosa

SÁBALO   SHAD

Gal: zamborca   *Por:* sável
Bas: kodak   *Fre:* alose
Cat: alatja   *Ger:* Alse, Maifisch

This shad, which the French distinguish as the 'true' shad, is mainly an Atlantic species, rare in the Mediterranean. Max <> 60, mkt <> 25–40.

All shad ascend rivers in about May to spawn (hence names meaning 'May fish'). Except for the problem which their very numerous small bones pose, they make good eating. In Portugal, sável is considered a great delicacy, plainly fried; but it is becoming rare.

In Galicia, the Miño seems to be the only river where these fish spawn.

Alosa fallax
SABOGA   TWAITE SHAD

Gal: /   *Por:* saboga
Bas: astun   *Fre:* alose finte
Cat: /   *Ger:* Finte

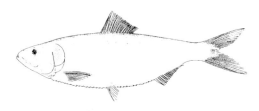

May be distinguished from the true shad by the six or more spots along each side. It is also a little smaller.

Family CLUPEIDAE

Sprattus sprattus

ESPADÍN   SPRAT

Gal: trancha, espadín   *Por:* espadilha, lavadilha
Bas: ijito-txardiña   *Fre:* sprat, esprot
Cat: meleta, amploia   *Ger:* Sprotte

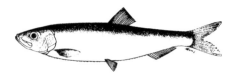

Max <> 14, mkt <> 12. The sprat resembles the sardine (see page 18) closely, but has sharp 'notches' along its belly. The season for fishing it is in May and June.

Sprats are available canned in northern Europe, but in Spain and Portugal (where they are not very common) they are usually fried.

Family ENGRAULIDAE

Engraulis encrasicolus

BOQUERÓN (ANCHOA   ANCHOVY
when conserved)

Gal: bocarte, bucareu   *Por:* anchova, biqueirão
Bas: antxoa, bokart   *Fre:* anchois
Cat: anxova, aladroc   *Ger:* Sardelle

Max <> 20, mkt <> 15. The home territory of this, the most famous of many species of anchovy around the world, is the Mediterranean, and the Atlantic up to the Bay of Biscay. Note the 'underslung' lower jaw, one easy way of telling anchovies apart from sardines.

Although anchovies can be eaten fresh, fried or grilled, they are commonly bought in salted form or (fillets of small ones) canned. Boquerón en Vinagre is a dish of pickled anchovy, especially good when prepared at home by marinating the fish in sherry vinegar. For larval anchovies and sardines (aladroch), see page 18.

Argentina sphyraena

PEZ PLATA   ARGENTINE

Gal: pión (de altura)
Bas: zilar arrain
Cat: l

Por: biqueirão branco
Fre: argentine
Ger: Glasauge

Max <> 45, mkt <> 10–20. The coloration is typical of pelagic fish, an olive green back and silvery sides, with a white belly tinged with green.

The argentine is not highly thought of in Spain, although it is sold in some markets and is even considered to be 'excellent' by some, while rejected by others. The explanation of this doubt about its quality seems to lie in the fragility of its flesh. It should be bought very fresh and cooked with care (frying works best).

Spanish fishing boats bring back argentines of another and somewhat larger species (max <> 55), with a more northerly range; this is *Argentina silus*. It may be met under the names pión or tomás in Galicia.

The silver pigment from the scales and swim bladder of the argentines has been used to produce something called 'essence of pearl', used in the manufacture of artificial pearls. However, this feature of these fish does not seem to have been exploited for culinary purposes.

Salmo salar

SALMÓN   SALMON

Gal: salmón   *Por:* salmão
Bas: izokin   *Fre:* saumon
Cat: salmó   *Ger:* Lachs

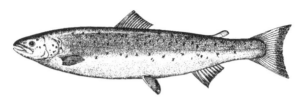

Max <> 150, mkt <> 40–80.

The good qualities of this famous and handsome fish are well known, as are the ways of preparing it. Wild salmon have become rare in the rivers of northern Portugal and the north of Spain which they used to frequent in large numbers. But they have retained a presence in many of the rivers and may now be making something of a comeback. Their place in the shops and markets has been usurped by the (often inferior, though sometimes very good) farmed salmon from northern countries.

If you find wild salmon on the menu in a restaurant, as I recently did in Santiago de Compostela, it will be expensive. The very first salmon of the season, known as 'campanu' in Santander and Asturias because the church bells are rung in honour of its capture, can fetch over £150 ($250) per kilo.

Salmo trutta

TRUCHA MARINA   SALMON TROUT

Gal: reo, bical   *Por:* truta marisca
Bas: itsas amuarrain   *Fre:* truite de mer
Cat: truita   *Ger:* Meerforel

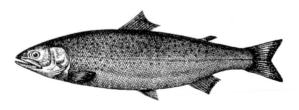

Very similar to the salmon (above) in appearance and habits, but smaller (max <> 100).

THE COD FAMILY

For European fish-eaters, this is one of the most important families of fish; but it is really a cold-water family, abounding in the North Atlantic and less well represented on the Iberian coast and in the Mediterranean. However, the cod itself, the most important species, is a prominent feature of the Spanish and Portuguese diets, as bacalao (see pages 28-9).

So far as fresh fish are concerned, the cod-like species which is most highly esteemed by Spaniards and Portuguese is the hake (page 31); but this is now assigned to a different but closely related family, Merluciidae.

It would be fair to say that, of the fish which are consumed in large quantities, bacalao and hake are the best beloved in the Iberian Peninsula.

Family GADIDAE

Trisopterus minutus

CAPELLAN, MOLLERA POOR COD

Gal: fodón
Bas: paneka txiki
Cat: capellà

Por: faneca
Fre: capelan
Ger: Zwergdorsch

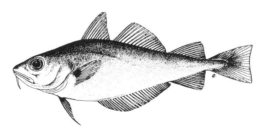

Max <> 25, mkt <> 12–16. A small member of the cod family, which occurs in two sub-species; that shown is *T m capelanus*, found in the northern part of the western basin of the Mediterranean. The bib or pout, *T m luscus*, which is **faneca** in Spanish and Portuguese, paneka in Basque, and tacaud in French, is more of an East Atlantic fish.

These relatively small fish are often disregarded as food, and it is true that they are only worth eating when very fresh; but the Atlantic species is well regarded in Galicia.

Merlangius merlangus

MERLÁN, PLEGONERO WHITING

Gal: bacalada
Bas: liba
Cat: peix rei

Por: badejo
Fre: merlan
Ger: Wittling

Max <> 70, mkt <> 30–40. Two sub-species are recognized; but both may be found in Iberian waters and the differences are minor. These are fish of variable coloration – the back may be brownish, bluish or greenish. There are three dorsal fins.

The flesh is easy to digest but lacking in flavour. Fry, poach or steam.

Micromesistius poutassou

BACALADILLA BLUE WHITING

Gal: lirio, bacaladilla
Bas: /
Cat: lluça, maira

Por: pichelim
Fre: poutassou
Ger: blauer Wittling

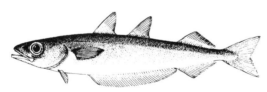

Max <> 50, mkt <> 30–40. A species of relatively deep waters. If very fresh, before its somewhat sour taste has developed, it may be cooked like the whiting; but most of the catch is usually turned into fish meal.

Phycis phycis and P blennioides

BROTOLA   **FORKBEARD**

Gal: bertorella, barbada lorcha   *Por:* abrótia
Bas: lotza   *Fre:* mostelle
Cat: mòllera, molla   *Ger:* Gabeldorsch

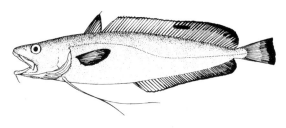

Max <> 80, mkt <> 20–30. The two species are very much alike, but *P blennioides* (shown above) is brownish while *P phycis* (below) is greyish and somewhat smaller.

Where common names differentiate between the two species, it is usual for *P phycis* to be given epithets meaning 'of the rocks' or 'of deep water'. It is rarely found in northern Spanish waters.

The forkbeards are quite good to eat, but the flesh is rather soft and they do not keep well. Frying is the best treatment.

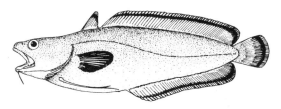

Gaidropsarus mediterraneus

BERTORELLA, BARBADA

THREE-BEARDED ROCKLING

Gal: barbada de pedra
Bas: aholatz
Cat: fura, oliana

Por: laibeque
Fre: motelle à trois barbillons
Ger: dreibärtelige Seequappe

Max <> 50, mkt <> 10–20, so quite a small fish from the cook's point of view, and a slim one too. Its usual fate is to be made into fish meal; but larger specimens are delicious if cleaned and cooked very fresh.

The same applies to two close relations, *G vulgaris* (Spanish **lota**, **barbada** or **bertorella**) and *G megalokynodon* (which can probably also bear any of these three Spanish names). As the drawings of them below indicate, these species have different patterns on their bodies, and *G vulgaris* has larger barbels. *Cilia mustela* is yet another, and smaller, species in this group, distinguished by having four barbels on its upper lip.

All these rocklings are apt to have local names meaning 'mother of eels'.

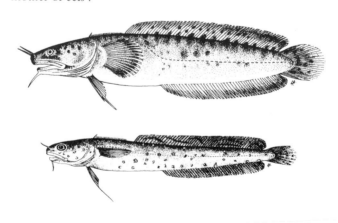

Molva molva

MARUCA   LING

Gal: maruca   *Por:* donzela
Bas: berruenda   *Fre:* lingue
Cat: escolá, peix de fonera   *Ger:* Leng

Max <> 200, mkt <> 75–150. This large fish is an Atlantic species, only occasionally reported from the West Mediterranean. It is more highly esteemed than the blue ling (below), and thought to be close to fresh cod in merit.

The dried and salted roe (huevas de maruca) constitutes a highly appreciated delicacy in, for example, the region of Almeria and Alicante.

Molva dipterygia (= M elongata)

ARBITAN, MARUCA (AZUL)   MEDITERRANEAN/ BLUE LING

Gal: palo, peixe pau   *Por:* donzela
Bas: berruenda txiki   *Fre:* lingue
Cat: /   *Ger:* Leng

Max <> 130, mkt <> 20–80. There are two sub-species, *M d d* and *M d macrophthalma*; and it is the latter which is found in Spanish waters.

Gadus morhua

BACALAO   COD

Gal: bacalao   *Por:* bacalhau
Bas: bakailao, makallo   *Fre:* cabillaud
Cat: bacallá   *Ger:* Dorsch, Kabeljauw

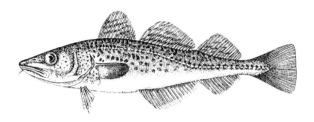

The cod of the North Atlantic has a maximum length of 150 cm, corresponding to a weight of 40 kg; but giants of this size are very rare – the usual length is in the range 35–90 cm.

A cod is a beautiful fish, whose aspect has been compared by an Irish author to that of Connemara marble, which typically exhibits green marbling on a near-white ground.

The range of the species extends as far south as the northern part of the Bay of Biscay, and fresh cod, caught in waters off Ireland, are landed by fishing vessels in the north of Spain; but it is not a fish of Spanish (or, still less, Portuguese) waters.

Yet it is, perhaps, the chief fish of both Spanish and Portuguese cookery, in cured form. There are two principal cures, of which the first is the one preferred in Spain and Portugal.

SALT COD is cod which has been salted, usually dry-salted (as opposed to being steeped in liquid brine), and then partially dried. After the salting, the water content of the fish will be just under 60%; after the drying, around 40%. Depending on the degree of treatment, it may have a white 'frost' of salt on it, or be creamy in colour.

STOCKFISH, much eaten in Italy and some other countries, is cod which has simply been dried. It is so dry – water content only about 15% – that it is hard like a stick.

Both salt cod and stockfish have their origins in early medieval times. Europeans, belonging to the Catholic faith and observing meatless days, needed a lot of fish, and stockfish from Norway was a valuable commodity as far back as the 10th century. But the huge supplies of cod off the North American coast, especially on the Newfoundland Banks, was not exploited until after Cabot 'discovered' Newfoundland in 1497. Then, the Europeans – with Portuguese, Spanish and French fishermen in the lead – began to exploit this resource seriously.

This plenitude of American cod represented great wealth for anyone who could conserve it and get it back to Europe. Simple drying wouldn't work on the damp and misty shores of Newfoundland, so the method adopted was dry-salting followed by drying. The cod were beheaded, split along the belly, cleaned, and rid of their backbones (except for a small piece by the tail). Then they were stacked with layers of salt between them, and the salt began to extract the water from them and replace it. Later, they would be dried.

The Portuguese may fairly claim to be number one nation in their enthusiasm for salt cod, which they call 'fiel amigo' (the faithful friend). Along the Rua do Arsenal in Lisbon, where the salt cod shops congregate most thickly, one can see for oneself what a thriving trade they have. Each establishment offers about a dozen different grades, with a fearsome guillotine-like contraption built into the serving counter, so that the merchant can slice off exactly what each customer wants.

PREPARING AND COOKING SALT COD

There are many different views about how much soaking in fresh water is needed to prepare salt cod for being cooked; but a middle-of-the-road position would be that it should soak for 18 hours, with three changes of water. Salt cod of the finest quality may be eaten raw, if wished, after this soaking. Otherwise the pieces may be cooked in any of hundreds of ways. The National Library in Lisbon possesses a book by the melodiously named Febrósia Mimoso, who boasts 'more than a hundred'; but then I found an anonymous work of 1927 which has 'more than three hundred'.

Typical Spanish dishes of salt cod include: Bacalao al Ajo Arriero (with fried garlic); Bacalao al Pil-pil (a Basque dish: the cooking is done with garlic and olive oil in a pan which is frequently shaken until a translucent white sauce has formed); Bacalao a la Vizcaina (with ham, red peppers and egg yolks among the ingredients of the sauce). Porrusalda is a dish of northern Spain (with potatoes and leeks – one might almost call it a salt cod version of Vichyssoise soup). In Majorca, squares of bacalao are floured and deep-fried, to be served with a tomato sauce.

The Portuguese also favour Bacalhau com Todos (cf Merluza com Todos, page 31); barbecued bacalhau, to be drenched with olive oil when served; Bacalhau Guisado (stewed – with potatoes, onion, tomato, etc); Bacalhau à Brás (fried with fried potatoes and a sort of scrambled egg topping); Bacalhau à Gomes de Sá, named after a salt cod merchant of Oporto, using milk to soften the salt cod; and Pataniscos, originally from the Algarve, which are fillets from a thick piece of salt cod, gently fried in batter.

Family GADIDAE
Pollachius pollachius
ABADEJO   POLLACK

Gal: badexo, serreta
Bas: abadiro, abadira
Cat: /

Por: juliana
Fre: lieu jaune
Ger: Pollack

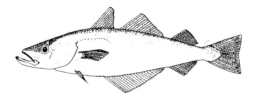

Max <> 130, mkt <> 50–80. An East Atlantic species, whose range extends as far south as Portugal, but not into the Mediterranean. A close relation, *P virens*, the saithe or coley (Galician fogonero), is even less disposed to venture south into Iberian waters, but apparently it sometimes reaches the northern coast of Spain. Both species are among those which may be dried to produce kinds of bacalao (see pages 28-9).

Melanogrammus aeglefinus
EGLEFINO   HADDOCK

Gal: burro
Bas: borriko
Cat: /

Por: arinca, burro
Fre: églefin
Ger: Schellfisch

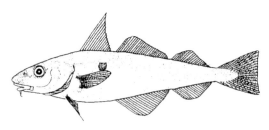

Max <> 110, mkt <> 50–75. A fish which is of some importance in the present context, although the northern coast of Spain represents the southern limit of its range. The main Spanish catch, like that of cod, comes from waters to the south of Ireland.

Haddock may appear in fish markets and (occasionally in cured form) on menus.

Merluccius merluccius

MERLUZA   HAKE

Gal: merluza, pescada,
pescadilla (small)
Bas: lebatz, legatz*
Cat: lluç

Por: pescada
Fre: merlu, merluche
Ger: Seehechte

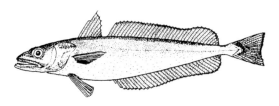

Max <> 120, mkt <> 30–70. The back is slate grey or bluish, and the inside of the mouth is black.

This is an excellent fish, near kin of the cod family, which occurs in both the Atlantic and the Mediterranean.

The Spanish and the Portuguese are the greatest enthusiasts for, and experts on preparing, the hake. The term 'pincho' is used in Galicia to indicate line-caught fish, rightly considered to be better than trawled ones.

Hake may be poached, steamed, baked or fried. Merluza in Salsa Verde (hake in green sauce) is a well-known dish, whose ingredients include garlic and potatoes and plenty of chopped parsley. Merluza a la Gallega is poached hake, with boiled onions and potatoes, served with a sweet pepper (pimiento dulce) sauce. Merluza Rellena is stuffed hake; the stuffing varies but often features chopped ham and hard-boiled egg. In the cider regions of northern Spain look for Merluza a la Sidra, hake cooked in cider. Down near Cadiz you may be lucky to find Caldillo de Perro ('dog soup', which combines hake and bitter Seville oranges).

The arrowhead-shaped flesh of the lower jaw is a delicacy: kokotxes in the Basque country, where one may find Kokotxes al Pil-pil (page 29) or in Salsa Verde (see above).

In Portugal, look for Filetes de Pescada (the fillets are marinated in lemon juice, garlic, salt, before being fried in a light batter); and Pescada com Todos ('hake with everything' – everything being greens in season plus carrot, onion, potato, hard-boiled egg, and a lacing of olive oil and wine vinegar at table).

★ small ones are legatz-tziki or legatz-kume

LIZARD-LIKE AND SNAKE-LIKE FISH

An unprepossessing group. A resemblance to lizards or snakes, or having a long beak, does not make for an attractive appearance in fish. However, the snake-like eels are of considerable gastronomic interest, not least when they are in larval form.

Family SYNODONTIDAE
Synodus saurus

PEZ DE SAN FRANCISCO | ## LIZARD FISH

Gal: l
Bas: San Franzisko arrain
Cat: dragó

Por: lagarto de rolo
Fre: lézard
Ger: Schneiderfisch

Max <> 45, mkt <> about 25. A fish of fairly deep water, named in many languages for its lizard-like head. Its distribution includes the Mediterranean, Morocco, and Atlantic islands.

A somewhat similar fish, shown at the foot of the page and belonging to the family Chlorophthalmidae, is *Chlorophthalmus agassizi*, **ojiverde** in Spanish, olho verde in Portuguese, green-eye in English. As one would expect, it has large and unmistakably green eyes.

The green-eye and the lizard fish are edible, and may be fried or used in fish soups, but that is just about all that can be said in their favour.

Much the same applies to the generally similar fish *Aulopus filamentosus*, of the family Aulopodidae; this has a dorsal fin whose second ray is greatly prolonged (in males, anyway), and is called **lagarto real** in Spanish. It does turn up in some Spanish markets.

Family ANGUILLIDAE

Anguilla anguilla

ANGUILA   COMMON EEL

Gal: anguía, eiroa
Bas: aingira
Cat: anguila

Por: eiró, enguia
Fre: anguille
Ger: Flussaal

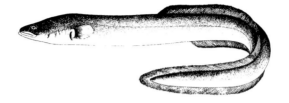

Max <> 150, mkt <> 30–80 (females larger than males). The extraordinary life cycle of this eel – born in the Sargasso Sea, crossing the Atlantic while still in larval form, assembling at the mouths of European rivers and then ascending them and living in them for almost all their adult life, but finally changing appearance and setting off back to the Sargasso Sea to spawn there and to die – is now well known but was a mystery until quite recently.

Farming of eels is carried out in various places, of which the most famous is probably Commacchio in Italy. The Albufera district on the Spanish Mediterranean coast is a rich ground for them. Well-known eel dishes in Portugal include Enguias Fritas (fried) and Caldeirada de Enguias (eel stew).

Tiny eels are so important gastronomically, and so unlike grown eels, that they need a sub-entry of their own:

ANGULA   ELVER

Gal: meixón, angula
Bas: txitxardin

Por: angula, enguia, meixão
Fre: civelle

The ways of cooking these tiny eels vary from one place to another. For example, Angulas al Estilo Vasco are swiftly cooked in very hot olive oil in which cloves of garlic have previously been fried. Earthenware dishes (the kind called 'barro') are used for cooking and serving, as they retain their heat well. A wooden spoon must be used for stirring the angulas in the hot oil. If a Spanish menu says simply 'Angulas', expect one of these earthenware dishes of them, with guindillas (tiny chilli peppers).

Family CONGRIDAE

Conger conger

CONGRIO   CONGER EEL

Gal: congrio, congro
Bas: itsas-aingira
Cat: congre

Por: congro, safio (small)
Fre: congre
Ger: Meeraal

Max <> 300, mkt <> 60–150. The colour varies according to habitat. Conger eels usually live in rocky crevices and wrecks, emerging at night to seek their prey. Prey may include octopus, an opponent with which most fish prefer not to tangle; but the conger is quite ready to do battle with it and is indeed its chief enemy. Even large congers may choose lurking places close inshore, so there is a possibility that bathers may inadvertently disturb one. If the conger disturbed is of a size close to the maximum, the experience will be terrifying.

In Asturias the name perengena is used, and in Andalucia the name zafio or polo.

The conger is notoriously bony, especially at the tail end, and for this reason a Galician author suggests that roasting or frying the fish is a mistake; it is better to boil it, then flake the flesh, free of bones, and use it in an empanada (shallow pie). Conger is one of the fish which is often served 'en Salsa Verde'.

In Galicia there is an unusual way of drying conger with large holes in its flesh, to increase circulation of air; this product is popular in Aragon.

34

Family MURAENIDAE
Muraena helena

MORENA MORAY EEL

Gal: moreia
Bas: itsasuge
Cat: murena

Por: moreia
Fre: murène
Ger: Muräne

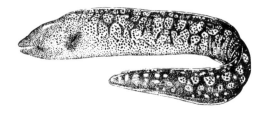

Max <> 130, mkt <> 60–100. The coloration and the pattern of light patches or spots on the darker background are highly variable. This is a sharp-toothed nocturnal predator which lurks in crevices between rocks by day and issues forth in search of prey at night.

The range of the moray eel is from Britain to Senegal in the East Atlantic and throughout the Mediterranean.

The tail end of the fish is full of small bones and best avoided. For those who prefer not to be reminded of the snake-like appearance of this species, it is best to poach sections and then remove the flesh from the bone and incorporate it in made-up dishes or pasties. Or the moray can go into fish soups, cut up into neat pieces.

For what it is worth, the practice in classical Rome was to poach or grill the fish and serve it with a sauce; but it is hard to discern any trace of Roman influence nowadays in Spain or the numerous other countries which were in the Roman Empire. However, in the city of Rome itself I met a clear indication that the veneration felt for the moray eel by the Romans of 2000 years ago has survived; for Professor Giorgio Bini himself, until his lamented death the greatest authority on fish of the Mediterranean, confided in me that the flesh of the moray is perhaps the finest of all fish in Italian waters.

Family SCOMBERESOCIDAE

Scomberesox saurus

PAPARDA   SKIPPER, SAURY

Gal: alcrique
Bas: botakar
Cat: trùnfau, aspet

Por: agulhão
Fre: balaou, aiguille de mer
Ger: Makrelenhechte

Max <> 50, mkt <> 30. A silver band running from the eye to near the tail separates the darker (olive-green or blue) back from the golden or silvery underside.

Skipper and kindred names are given to the fish because it 'skips' out of the water when evading pursuit.

Good eating, but not of commercial importance. Classified in Spain as pescado azul (see page 10).

Family BELONIDAE

Belone belone

AGUJA, SALTÓN   GAR-FISH

Gal: agulla
Bas: orratz
Cat: agulla

Por: agulha
Fre: aiguille
Ger: Hornhecht

Max <> 95, mkt <> 40–50. The bones of this fish turn green when it is cooked, and this, plus what is regarded as its generally repulsive aspect, puts many people off eating it (although it is perfectly wholesome). To be fried, or grilled, or used in fish soups.

FLYING FISH

Here is a group of fish set apart from all others by its seeming ability to fly. In fact, it does not fly; its large pectoral fins can be extended like wings, but instead of flapping like those of a bird they stay in a fixed position and the fish merely glides, after a spurt of very vigorous swimming has propelled it upwards clear of the water. But the glide may be quite prolonged and swift. I had occasion in S E Asia to hear, from an observer well qualified to record such details, that a flying fish observed by him had maintained a speed of 40 kph for 30 seconds, but accelerating occasionally to as much as 65 kph. This acceleration is interesting. The gliding fish allows itself to lose height (from the typical gliding height of about 30 cm) until its tail is just in the water again. Very rapid vibration of the tail will then produce, within a second, a high degree of acceleration.

Family EXOCOETIDAE

Hirundichthys (formerly *Cypselurus*) *rondeletii*

PEZ VOLADOR, JURIOLA

FLYING FISH

Gal: peixe volador
Bas: arrain hegalari
Cat: orenyola

Por: peixe voador
Fre: poisson volant
Ger: Flugfisch

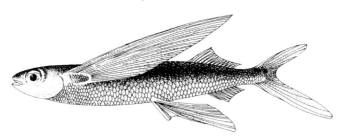

Max <> 30, mkt <> 15–25. Has black 'wings' (in reality, extended pectoral fins).

There is a whole tribe of flying fish, including species in the genus *Cheilopogon*, which closely resemble each other and usually share the names given here (plus a few others such as the Galician sardiña voladora). There is also a 'flying fish' in the gurnard family.

Moderately good to eat.

A MIXED BAG

Before the catalogue arrives at the very extensive and important order Perciformes, it lists a miscellany of species in five families. The most interesting are the John Dory and the opah. Few readers are likely to see the latter; but the former is common in the markets and should not be rejected because of its quaint and angular appearance.

The sand smelts provide an exceptionally striking example of confusion in nomenclature (both scientific and vernacular), and anyone who wrestles with this tangle is apt to start wondering whether there is really any point in distinguishing between the various species.

Family ATHERINIDAE
Atherina presbyter

PEJERREY   SAND SMELT

Gal: pión, piardo
Bas: odolgabe arrain
Cat: abichón

Por: peixe-rei
Fre: prêtre
Ger: Priesterfisch

Max <> 21, mkt <> 10–12. *Atherina presbyter* is the largest of the several sand smelts in Iberian waters. These small fish are as often used for bait as for human food. In the latter event they are usually fried.

The two other noteworthy sand smelts are:

A hepsetus; Spanish **chuleto**, Catalan chuclet or xauclet; French siouclet or sauclet; max <> 20, mkt <> 12–15.

A (hepsetia) boyeri (= *A mochon*); Spanish **abichón, mochón**; Basque kauxua; Catalan xanguet, cabeçuda, moixonet; Galicia pión, piardo, bucareo; French joël; max <> 13. This is the species illustrated below.

However, note also that: alternative Spanish names for *A boyeri* (or perhaps for all three species) are bocón and aguacioso; and that Catalan names for one, two, or three of them include peix sense sang (cf xanguet).

Family SPHYRAENIDAE

Sphyraena sphyraena

ESPETÓN   BARRACUDA

Gal: barracuda   *Por:* bicuda
Bas: /   *Fre:* brochet de mer
Cat: espet   *Ger:* Pfeilhecht

Max <> 165, mkt <> 30–50. A voracious fish, often sought by anglers; uncommon in fish markets, but good to eat.

Fillets may be fried; otherwise I have found few recommendations for ways of cooking these fish.

Zeus faber

PEZ DE SAN PEDRO   JOHN DORY

Gal: Samartiño, San Pedro   *Por:* peixe São Pedro
Bas: olarra, muxumartin   *Fre:* Saint-Pierre
Cat: gall, gallo   *Ger:* Heringskönig

Max <> 65, mkt <> 15–50. The black spot on each side is the reason for this bizarre-looking fish to be called by the name of St Peter – the idea being that the marks were left by St Peter's fingers when he lifted the fish up from the Sea of Galilee (which he could not have done, since the John Dory could not have been there). 'John Dory' itself is a name for which no certain derivation has been established. (I think myself that a better sort of name is the Turkish one, dülger; this likens the fish to a set of carpenter's tools, a resemblance which is well observed.)

Despite its unpromising appearance, the John Dory makes very good eating – there is, admittedly, a higher proportion of waste than usual, but the fillets which can be lifted from the body are exceptionally good. I am told that in most parts of Portugal and Spain the merits of this fish are fully recognized, but that in Galicia, for reasons connected with its uncouth look, this is not the case.

Bullit de Peix, a Catalan boiled fish dish, often features John Dory as an ingredient.

Lampris guttatus (= *L luna*)

LUNA REAL   OPAH

Gal: peixe luia   *Por:* cravo, mariposa
Bas: opah   *Fre:* opah
Cat: I   *Ger:* Gotteslachs

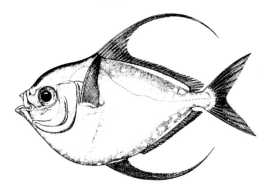

Although it may reach a length of 2 metres, this majestic ocean fish, which is found all round the world, is usually between 60 and 120 cm long. The coloration is striking. An English writer, Jane Grigson, described it as having a body 'softly spotted with white. The main blue-grey and green of its skin reflects an iridescence of rose, purple and gold. The fins are a brilliant red. The sickle tail has reminded people of the moon's shape; the ribs of its fins have seemed like the scarlet rays of the sun.'

Rarely caught and therefore rarely seen in the markets; but very good indeed, so to be bought at once when it does appear! The flesh is pink and firm, with a fine flavour carrying hints of salmon and tuna or, as some say, of veal. Provided that it is very fresh, this flesh may be sliced thin and eaten raw. Or escalopes may be fried. A whole shoulder can be roasted. Steaks cut from the upper rear part of the body are especially good if grilled.

Beryx decadactylus

PALOMETA ROJA, REY DEL BESUGO

ALFONSINO

Gal: castañeta encarnada
Bas: /
Cat: bishigu errege

Por: imperador
Fre: dorade rouge, béryx
Ger: Kaiserbarsch

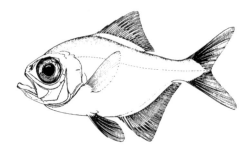

Max <> over 40 (possibly up to 60), mkt <> 20–35.

A fish of the deeper waters and a great traveller. It ranges as far north as Norway and also occurs in the West Atlantic and (occasionally) in the vicinity of Japan, Hawaii, and Tasmania.

B splendens, shown below, is a close relation, smaller, found off the Portuguese coast, and in Galician waters. The Galician name, 'macho (de palometa)' does not signify a male fish, as one might suppose, but denotes any fish of this species. The corresponding name 'femia (de palometa)' signifies *B decadactylus*, whether female or male.

Both species may be called alfonsim in Portuguese.

The flesh is highly esteemed, especially in Galicia. Suitable for any of the standard ways of cooking fish.

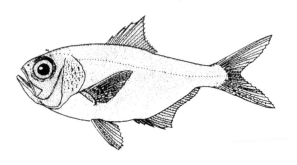

THE SEA BASS AND GROUPER FAMILY

Here we arrive at the very important order Perciformes, the perch-like fish. Perch-like means (among other things) that the fish have at least some spiny fins, and that some of the leading rays of the dorsal and anal fins are thickened and unjointed and (usually) sharp. The pectoral fins are high up on the body; whereas more primitive fish in other orders have markedly low-slung pectorals. The pelvic fins normally have one spiny ray each and are well forward on the body.

This first batch includes several groupers. Species of grouper abound in the Indo-Pacific and the Caribbean, but the family is sparsely represented in the Mediterranean and the East Atlantic. Let us, however, be thankful for what we have; they make fine eating.

Family MORONIDAE

Dicentrarchus labrax

LUBINA   SEA BASS

Gal: robaliza (small),robalo (large)
Bas: lupina, lupia
Cat: llobarro

Por: robalo
Fre: bar
Ger: Seebarsch

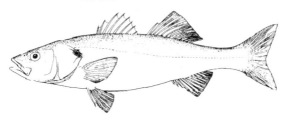

Max <> 100, mkt <> 20–55. A handsome, silvery, voracious fish which is a favoured prey of anglers.

Young specimens may have spots on their sides. But adult sea bass which have spots, lots of small ones, are of a closely related and slightly smaller species, *D punctatus*. This species, which is **baila** in Spanish and llobarro pigallat in Catalan, is shown overleaf.

In connection with the Galician names given above, I should remark that these names and the related name robaloa have different meanings in different regions of Spain. Sometimes they are used to distinguish male and female. And in parts of the south the name robalo refers to juvenile specimens, not full-grown adults.

The firm flesh, free of small bones, makes this fish a good choice for dishes in which a substantial fish is presented whole, eg poached, skinned and masked with mayonnaise.

Before we pass on to the next family, here is a drawing of the spotted sea bass, referred to on the preceding page.

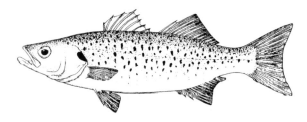

Family SERRANIDAE
Polyprion americanum

CHERNA   WRECKFISH

Gal: mero, charla	*Por:* cherne
Bas: mero beltz	*Fre:* cernier
Cat: rascàs	*Ger:* Wrackbarsch

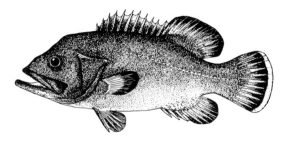

Max <> 200, mkt <> 60–90. A greyish fish which takes its name from its habit of lurking in wrecked ships or similar debris. It is never taken in large numbers.

Steaks or fillets may be grilled, fried, poached, or baked.

Epinephelus guaza

MERO   GROUPER

Gal: mero   *Por:* mero
Bas: mero (zuri)   *Fre:* mérou
Cat: anfós   *Ger:* brauner Zachenbarsch

A large and long-lived fish, whose length may be well over 1 metre by the time it attains the age of 40 or so. However, the usual length is 20–80 cm, and few specimens nowadays survive to old age. Coloration is usually a reddish or yellowish brown, with dark patches (*epinephelus* means 'with clouds upon it').

Of all the groupers taken in the Mediterranean, this species accounts for half.

Highly esteemed. There is a saying: 'de la mar el mero, de la tierra el carnero': from the sea, the grouper, from the land, the lamb. Small ones may be baked whole; otherwise take steaks or fillets and cook them as you please.

Two recipes which I chose for inclusion in my book *Mediterranean Seafood* are Mero a la Naranja (with an orange sauce) and Mero con Salsa de Almendra (with an almond sauce); both make delicious dishes.

Family SERRANIDAE

Epinephelus aeneus

CHERNE DE LEY GROUPER

Gal: / Por: garoupa (verde)
Bas: / Fre: mérou (blanc)
Cat: / Ger: Zackenbarsch

Max <> just over 1 metre, mkt <> 30–80. Coloration varies; it may be reddish brown or (as the most common Portuguese name indicates) greenish, the body often indistinctly marked by broad diagonal pale bands, and the lower part of the head almost always marked by narrow whiteish lines sloping downwards.

Rare in Iberian waters; met in the far south only.

Epinephelus caninus

CHERNE DENTÓN GROUPER

Gal: / Por: mero gigante
Bas: / Fre: mérou noir
Cat: / Ger: /

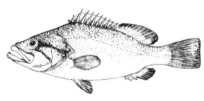

Max <> almost 160, mkt <> 30–100; so, the largest Mediterranean grouper, which justifies the Portuguese name. The colour is generally dark, and all except elderly specimens are likely to exhibit the slanting dark lines behind the eyes which can be seen in the drawing.

Not common in Iberian waters, and not known at all on Spain's northern coast.

Epinephelus alexandrinus

FALSO ABADEJO GROUPER

Gal: / *Por: mero amarelo*
Bas: / *Fre: badèche*
Cat: / *Ger: /*

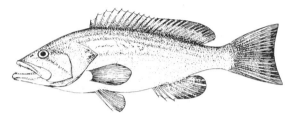

Max <> over 1 metre, some say 140, mkt <> 30–70. Rare in Spanish waters; may be met in the south only.

Mycteroperca rubra

GITANO GROUPER

Gal: / *Por: garoupa chumbo*
Bas: / *Fre: abadèche rouge*
Cat: / *Ger: rote Zackenbarsch*

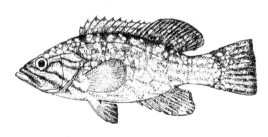

Max <> 80, mkt <> 20–40. A smaller grouper, usually reddish in colour with a pale dappling of marks of various shapes.

The flesh is of good quality, but is said to be capable of harbouring toxins; so it is better to buy this fish from a knowledgeable merchant rather than from an unlicensed urchin.

Serranus cabrilla

CABRILLA   COMBER

Gal: cabra
Bas: kraba
Cat: serrá, mero bord

Por: serrano alecrim
Fre: serran
Ger: Blutstriemen

Max <> 40, mkt <> 25–30. A reddish fish marked with vertical bands and some horizontal stripes below.

One Spanish author remarks succinctly of this fish: 'muy bueno.' Certainly, it is greatly appreciated in Galicia. It has the good qualities of its near relations, the groupers (see the two preceding pages), but the advantage of being of a more easily manageable size.

Serranus atricauda

SERRANO IMPERIAL   COMBER

Gal: /
Bas: kraba inperial
Cat: /

Por: serrano de rolo
Fre: serran à queue noire
Ger: /

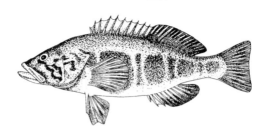

Max <> 35, mkt <> 20–30. Distinguished by the pattern, shown clearly in the drawing, of dark rectangles alternating with vertical dark bars on its sides. The tail is black, or at least its tips are, which accounts for the specific name *atricauda*.

Family SERRANIDAE
Serranus scriba
SERRANO COMBER

Gal: cabra   *Por:* serrano pequeno
Bas: kraba   *Fre:* serran écriture
Cat: serrá, serranet   *Ger:* Schriftbarsch

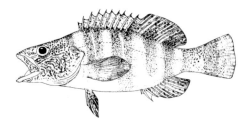

Max <> 35, mkt <> 20–25. There is no real English name for this species, but 'lettered perch' has sometimes been used; this and some names in other languages refer to the marks like scribbling which the fish bears on its sides.

   S scriba is more common in the Mediterranean than in the Atlantic.

Serranus hepatus
MERILLO BROWN COMBER

Gal: /   *Por:* serrano ferreiro
Bas: /   *Fre:* tambour
Cat: serrá de bou   *Ger:* Beutelbarsch

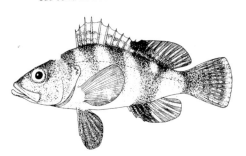

Max <> 25, mkt <> 10–15. The smallest of the four combers listed here.

   These are very good when fried, but they can also be poached or baked.

DRUMS, SCAD AND JACKS ETC, BLUEFISH, DOLPHIN FISH, RAY'S BREAM

The families Sciaenidae (mostly known as 'drums' in other parts of the world, because of the noise they make under the water) and Carangidae (called jacks for reasons which have eluded me so far) are tolerably well represented in the Mediterranean, although there are fewer species than in, say, the Caribbean. After them come the exceptionally voracious, even bloodthirsty, bluefish; the circumglobal dolphin fish (nothing to do with the mammal called dolphin), and the 'oddball' Ray's bream, which acts as a curtain-raiser, so to speak, for the following section of the catalogue, which deals with sea breams proper.

Family SCIAENIDAE
Umbrina cirrosa

VERRUGATO (OMBRINE)

Gal: gato de mar, burrugato
Bas: berrugeta
Cat: corvall

Por: calafate
Fre: ombrine
Ger: /

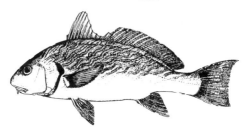

Max <> 100, mkt <> 30–80. The 'ombrine' (I have always found it convenient to adopt the French name into English, which has no real name for the species) is easily recognized by the diagonal wavy lines on its yellowish sides. These thin lines are blue bordered with black and there may be up to 30 of them.

This species is found throughout the Mediterranean and in the East Atlantic. Two close relations, both somewhat smaller, are absent from the East Mediterranean. These are *U canariensis* (Spanish, **verrugato de Canarias**; Portuguese, calafate) and *U ronchus* (Spanish, **verrugato de fango**; Portuguese, again calafate).

A good fish. To be grilled, fried in slices, or baked.

Family SCIAENIDAE
Argyrosomus regius

CORVINA   MEAGRE

Gal: corbina
Bas: arrano-berrugeta
Cat: (corb) reig

Por: corvina
Fre: maigre, sciène
Ger: /

Max <> 200, mkt <> about 100; so, a large fish. It has a golden throat. Although present throughout the Mediterranean and in the East Atlantic from Denmark down to the Congo, it seems now to be caught mainly in Turkey. Back in the early 1950s, however, local fishermen in the Cadiz area caught 99 in a single day.

Good fare. Stew with potatoes; or serve with Salsa Verde; or cut steaks and fry them.

Sciaena umbra

CORVALLO   CORB

Gal: /
Bas: berrugeta ilun
Cat: corball de roca

Por: corvina preta
Fre: corb
Ger: Schattenfisch

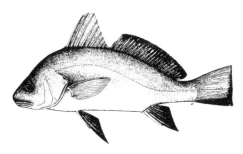

Max <> 70, mkt <> 20–40. A fish which lurks in rocky places, as the Catalan name suggests, and is of nocturnal habit.

This is one of the smaller drums, and is suitable for being cooked whole.

Trachurus trachurus

CHICHARRO, JUREL

HORSE MACKEREL, SCAD

Gal: xurelo
Bas: txitxarro
Cat: sorell

Por: chicharro, carapau (small)
Fre: chinchard
Ger: Stöcker

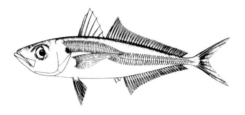

Market length varies from quite small to 20–35 cm. This species has two close relations (*T mediterraneus* and *T picturatus*) which only ichthyologists bother to distinguish from it. The fact is that these fish are lacking in succulence and have only modest attraction on the table.

Grill or fry. Small specimens can go in fish soups, though they won't contribute much to it.

All the above applies also to *Caranx* (= *Decapterus*) *rhonchus,* a species of the North African and North-West African coasts, which no doubt swims into Spanish waters from time to time – anyway, it has a Spanish name, **jurel real** (despite the apparent absence of any characteristics which would justify counting it as a 'royal' fish). The drawing of it below shows in what minor respects it differs in appearance from the true horse mackerel.

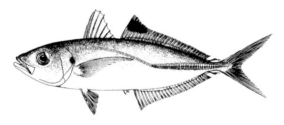

Family CARANGIDAE
Seriola dumerili

Pez Limón   Amberjack

Gal: /
Bas: /
Cat: sirviola, verderol (young)

Por: charuteiro
Fre: sériole
Ger: Seriolafisch

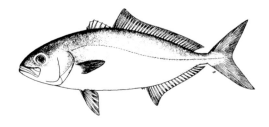

Max <> (exceptionally) near to 200, mkt <> only 30–60. A fine looking fish with a dark bluish back and a yellow streak, more or less noticeable, running along each side from cheek to tail. The tail of young specimens is markedly yellow; hence the Catalan name, verderol, for these youngsters.

The amberjack is a loner, not caught in large numbers and of minor importance commercially. It occurs in the West Atlantic too, as far north as the Chesapeake Bay, and is called rudderfish by Americans.

Quite a good fish, but apt to vary in edible quality – I recall eating one which was delicious, but also another which lacked succulence and flavour. This ambivalent verdict would not be applauded in Majorca. The people there are very enthusiastic about amberjack, especially when prepared a la Mallorquina; and the species is now being farmed at Puerto de Andraitx.

Lichia amia

PALOMETÓN LEERFISH

Gal: / *Por:* palombeta, doirada
Bas: / *Fre:* liche
Cat: palomida, sorell de penya *Ger:* /

Max <> 200, mkt <> 40–100. A fish of coastal and estuarine waters; brownish above, silvery below.

The flesh is firm and compact. It is suitable, when very fresh, for being eaten raw, Japanese-style, or uncooked but marinated in lemon juice. However, it is normally cooked, in steaks.

Naucrates ductor

PEZ PILOTO PILOT FISH

Gal: piloto *Por:* peixe-piloto
Bas: / *Fre:* poisson pilote
Cat: / *Ger:* Lotsenfisch

Max <> 65, mkt <> around 35–40. Most names for this fish reflect its habit of following ships or swimming in front of sharks, as though being a pilot. Not a fish to be found in any market, since it is quite choosy about its habitat. In the Mediterranean, it favours Malta and the Balearic Islands, where it is available in abundance during the summer.

Good white flesh, suitable for grilling or poaching.

Trachinotus ovatus

PALOMETA (BLANCA), POMPANO
PAMPANO BLANCO

Gal: castañeta branca   *Por:* sereia
Bas: /   *Fre:* palomine
Cat: palomida, xica   *Ger:* Bläuel

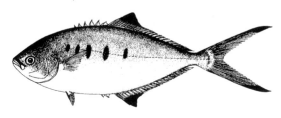

Max <> 70, mkt <> 25–35. A Mediterranean and East Atlantic representative of a genus better known in West Atlantic waters. Indeed the name pompano is American rather than English.

These are fish which travel in schools, so may be available in quantity. The white and compact flesh has a fine flavour; and the size and shape of the fish facilitate taking head-to-tail fillets.

Family POMATOMIDAE
Pomatomus saltatrix

ANJOVA   BLUEFISH

Gal: /   *Por:* anchova
Bas: /   *Fre:* tassergal
Cat: tallahams, trenca-hams   *Ger:* /

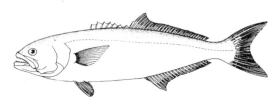

Max <> 110, mkt <> 20–75. The blue fish (or 'blues', as they are called in North America) are the terror of smaller fish, which they hunt and devour 'like a pack of hungry wolves'.

Bluefish are themselves eaten with the greatest appreciation in Turkey and in the USA. There is less enthusiasm for them in Spain and Portugal. The flesh is quite rich. They are best grilled or baked.

Family CORYPHAENIDAE
Coryphaena hippurus

LAMPUGA   DOLPHIN FISH

Gal: /
Bas: lemorratz
Cat: llampuga, dourat

Por: doirado
Fre: coriphène
Ger: Goldmakrele

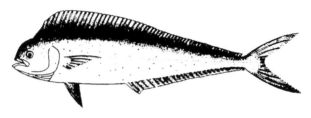

Although specimens of 2 metres in length have been recorded, this is quite exceptional and market length is usually 40–90 cm. A remarkably pretty fish when in the water or just taken from it; the colour is then silvery and gold, with iridescent flashes of blue and green.

The dolphin fish is an oceanic fish which occurs all round the world. Americans will be familiar with it as mahi-mahi, the name by which it is known in Hawaii, where it is plentiful. In the Mediterranean it seems to be most common in the vicinity of Malta, no doubt because the characteristics of the waters round that island suit its habits. It is not to be confused with the dolphin, which is a marine mammal, not a fish.

Excellent fare, with a good flavour. Steaks may be fried or grilled; and the smaller specimens respond well to being baked.

THE SEA BREAMS

The true sea breams belong to the family Sparidae, which is strongly represented in the Mediterranean. For reasons which go far back in the history of that sea, there are numerous different species – and many of them, although they occur in the Atlantic at similar latitudes, are not found in that ocean as far north as the Bay of Biscay.

However, this part of the catalogue begins with a species of the family Bramidae, which bears the name of bream but differs in a number of ways from the true sea breams – and is, incidentally, a remarkably interesting and delicious fish. Then comes a species of the family Haemulidae (a family whose members are often referred to as 'grunts'). After it come the numerous Sparidae tribe, and after them the somewhat similar picarels.

Family BRAMIDAE
Brama brama (formerly *B raji*)

JAPUTA   RAY'S BREAM

Gal: castañeta (negra), palometa
Bas: papardo
Cat: castagnola

Por: chaputa, freira
Fre: castagnole
Ger: Brachsenmakrele

Max <> 70, mkt <> 30–50. A noble and solitary fish which is not commonly found in the markets, although the deep waters off the Iberian coasts seem to have more than their fair share of the species.

The curious English name honours the great naturalist John Ray (1628-1705).

A really good fish. If you see japuta on the menu, opt for it. If you buy one to cook, it may be poached or grilled. Fillets may be fried or baked in white wine with flavourings.

Plectorhinchus mediterraneus
(= *Parapristipoma mediterraneum*)

BURRO, BORRIQUETE   RUBBER-LIP GRUNT

Gal: burro   *Por:* pombo, mulato
Bas: /   *Fre:* dorade grise
Cat: /   *Ger:* /

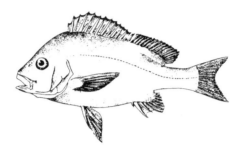

Max <> 80, mkt <> 30–60. A fish which usually has a dark brown or violet grey back. Distribution: much of the West African coast, the Canaries, and north to Portugal.

This species has had a major identity crisis in the annals of ichthyology. Besides the two generic names quoted above, it has in relatively recent times been assigned also to *Diagramma* and to *Gaterin*.

A related species, *Pomadasys incisus*, may be found in the vicinity of the Strait of Gibraltar and further south. It is smaller (max <> 50) and has the name **roncador** in both Spanish and Portuguese. Although it is something of a rarity in Spanish markets, a drawing of it is shown below.

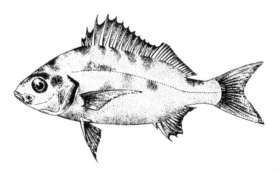

Family SPARIDAE
Sparus aurata
DORADA   GILT-HEAD BREAM

Gal: dourada
Bas: urreburu
Cat: orada

Por: dourada
Fre: daurade
Ger: Goldbrassen

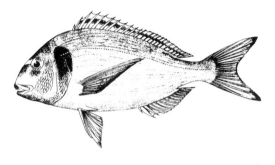

Max <> 70, mkt <> 25–45. Generally regarded as the finest member of its family. There is a golden spot on each cheek, and a crescent-shaped golden mark on the brow of this august creature. Most names refer to this feature; the Basque name, for example, means 'gold head'.

The excellence of this species and its ability to thrive in waters less salty than the open sea are such that it is now being cultured on quite a large scale in, for example, Greece. Fish reared in this way may exhibit small deviations from the norm in such things as their scale count, and are held by some to have a flavour and a texture which compare unfavourably with those of fish taken from the wild. Much presumably depends on what conditions prevail in each particular 'fish farm'.

A gilt-head may be filleted or cooked whole. Grilling, baking (Dorada al Horno), frying, poaching, steaming – all are suitable. Dorada a la Sal (the cleaned but otherwise whole fish is cooked in a thick 'jacket' of sea salt – and when the jacket is broken, the skin peels off with it, leaving the succulent flesh exposed) is a well-known dish of Andalucia.

Pagrus pagrus

PARGO SEA BREAM

Gal: pargo, prago
Bas: gurbin, mutur motz
Cat: pagre

Por: pargo (comum)
Fre: pagre (commun)
Ger: (gemeiner) Rotbrassen

Max <> 80, mkt <> 20–60. Although this species bears many names of the 'common sea bream' sort, and indeed is a common fish in the Mediterranean and East Atlantic, its merits are considerable. Gastronomic considerations apart, one must be impressed by its feat in establishing itself in the West Atlantic (thanks to the coincidence that the time its eggs take to hatch is about the same as the time that they take to drift over to the Caribbean on the westerly current).

The flesh is of fine quality, though not esteemed quite as highly as that of the gilt-head bream (page 59). It is very good if poached and served with boiled potatoes laced with olive oil (as in Portugal); or it can be given any of the standard treatments. However, it is quite delicate and should be very fresh; otherwise it will acquire a peculiar taste which the Portuguese call 'fénico'.

Pagrus auriga

HURTA RED-BANDED SEA BREAM

Gal: sama, samba
Bas: /
Cat: /

Por: pargo sêmola
Fre: pagre rayé, sar royal
Ger: /

Max <> 80, mkt <> 25–40. This species (opposite, above) and *P caeruleosticus* (opposite, below), both close relations of *P pagrus*, have caused considerable perplexity, and their classification has changed many times. The current view may be expressed in a simple rule of thumb: if it has broad vertical

reddish bands (fainter in adults, and fading after death), it is
P auriga; but if it has blue spots on its sides, it is *P caeruleosticus*.

This fish is well known on the Cadiz coast, although not
abundant in the markets (because not easy to catch, being rock
fish). Rota, just opposite Cadiz, is famous for its Hurta a la
Rotena, baked in an earthenware 'barro' with tomatoes, onions
and peppers; but it may be even better (according to Mauricio
González-Gordon) if baked on a bed of onion and potato slices
with olive oil and sherry and a couple of pieces of 'tocino de
jamon' – plus tomato, green pepper and lemon slices inserted
into gashes in the side. I have seen the Spanish Castilian name
spelled 'urta' in some menus, eg Urta a la Plancha.

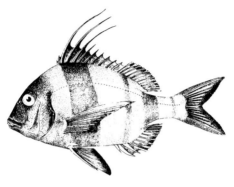

Pagrus caeruleosticus (= Sparus ehrenbergi)

ZAPATA   BLUE-SPOTTED SEA BREAM

Gal: /	Por: pargo, ruço
Bas: /	Fre: pagre à points bleus
Cat: /	Ger: /

Max <> 90, mkt <> 30–50, so slightly larger than the preceding species. Again, flesh of fine quality, comparable to that of
the gilt-head bream (page 59) in texture and flavour.

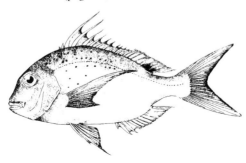

Dentex dentex

DENTÓN DENTEX

Gal: dentón   *Por:* dentão
Bas: txelba   *Fre:* denté
Cat: déntol   *Ger:* Zahnbrassen

Max <> 100, mkt <> 20–50. Another large and noble sea bream, which is found throughout the Mediterranean and also, to some extent, in the East Atlantic. Colour changes, with age, from grey to a somewhat rosy hue and then to a bluish grey; and the number and disposition of the dark spots vary.

From my own experience I judge that specimens of about 25 to 35 cm make the best eating. A dentex of that size, cleaned and baked in a large vessel with plenty of aromatics, makes a fine dish.

Dentex gibbosus (or *D filosus*)

SAMA DE PLUMA (PINK) DENTEX

Gal: /   *Por:* capatão de bandeira
Bas: /   *Fre:* gros denté rose
Cat: corcovada   *Ger:* /

Max <> 100, mkt <> around 50, so as large as the regular dentex (above), from which it may be distinguished by the long 3rd and 4th rays of the dorsal spine, and (in mature specimens) by a jutting 'forehead' which gives the fish a learned look. The illustration at the top of the next page is of a fairly young specimen and does not yet have this appearance.

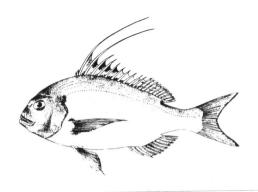

Dentex macrophthalmus

CACHUCHO   LARGE-EYED DENTEX

Gal: /   *Por:* cachucho
Bas: /   *Fre:* denté à gros yeux
Cat: pagel dentó   *Ger:* /

Max <> 40, mkt <> 20–25. This smaller species can be distinguished by its relatively large eyes. (Note, however, that one more dentex, *D maroccanus*, also has large eyes. Its Spanish names are **sama** or **chacarona**.) This is a cheap fish, which must be absolutely fresh if it is to avoid having the 'fénico' taste referred to on page 60; but it can be quite good fried. It is sometimes called rubiel in Spain.

Both this and the preceding species are found in the southern waters of the Mediterranean and in the East Atlantic (but not very far north).

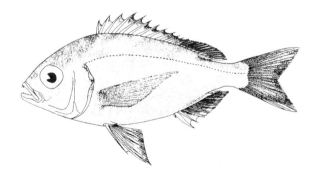

Diplodus sargus

SARGO   WHITE SEA BREAM

Gal: sargo
Bas: txarbo
Cat: sard

Por: sargo
Fre: sar commun
Ger: grosser Geissbrassen

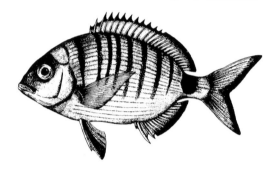

Max <> 45, mkt <> 15–30. Recognition points are well shown in the drawing. This fish and the one below are highly appreciated in Galicia.

Diplodus vulgaris

MOJARRA   TWO-BANDED BREAM

Gal: chaparella
Bas: mutxarra
Cat: variada

Por: mucharra
Fre: sar doré
Ger: gemeiner Geissbrassen

Max <> 45, mkt <> 18–25.

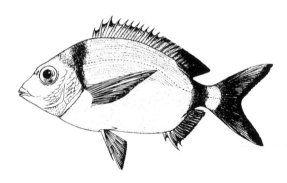

Diplodus cervinus (= D trifasciatus)

SARGO BREADO, (SARGO) SOLDADO

(ZEBRA) SEA BREAM

Gal: sargo acastañado
Bas: /
Cat: /

Por: sargo veado
Fre: sar à grosses lèvres
Ger: /

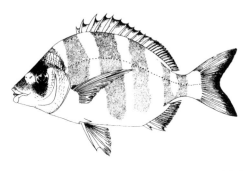

Max <> 55, mkt 20–35. This distinctively marked fish occurs throughout the Mediterranean and also in the East Atlantic, but is uncommon in northern Spanish waters.

Diplodus (formerly Puntazzo) puntazzo

MORRUDA, SARGO PICUDO

SHEEPSHEAD BREAM

Gal: sargo picudo
Bas: akermujoie, muxoin
Cat: morruda

Por: sargo bicudo
Fre: sar tambour
Ger: Spitzbrassen

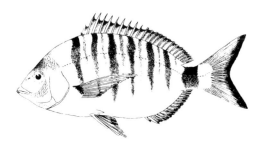

Max <> 60, mkt <> 15–30. A fish which is regarded highly enough to have warranted experiments in culturing it in fish farms. Another species which is not common in northern Spanish waters.

Diplodus annularis

RASPALLÓN   ANNULAR BREAM

Gal: l
Bas: bustanbeltz, mutxarra
Cat: esparrall

Por: alcarraz
Fre: sparaillon
Ger: Ringelbrassen

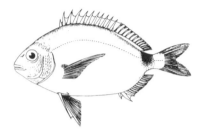

Max <> 24, mkt <> 8–18; the smallest of its group, but good. Frying is recommended.

Oblada melanura

OBLADA   SADDLED BREAM

Gal: l
Bas: bustanbeltz, kollaka
Cat: oblada

Por: dobradiça
Fre: oblade
Ger: Bandbrasse

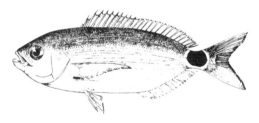

Max <> 30, mkt <> 15–20. Best in the spring. Grill, fry, or use in fish soups.

Boops (formerly *Box*) *boops*

BOGA   BOGUE

Gal: boga
Bas: boga
Cat: boga

Por: boga-do-mar
Fre: bogue
Ger: Gelbstriemen

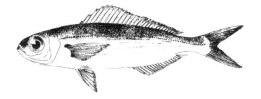

Max <> 35, mkt <> 10–25. Boops is not pronounced like 'oops' (the exclamation one makes on dropping something) but as 'boe-ops', and means ox-eyed, which is to say large-eyed. The species has a substantial presence in most Mediterranean fish markets, but is of only moderately good quality (although one authority points out that the quality varies according to what it has been feeding on).

Lithognathus (formerly *Pagellus*) *mormyrus*

HERRERA   STRIPED BREAM

Gal: /
Bas: erla
Cat: mabra, mabre

Por: ferreira
Fre: marbré
Ger: Marmorbrassen

Max <> 55, mkt <> 15–30. The 14 or 15 dark vertical bands are an instant recognition point. The Basque name means 'bee' with reference to this, but the species is rare in northern Spanish waters.

One of the better members of the family. Grilling is recommended.

Pagellus bogaraveo
(= *P centrodontus*, *P cantabricus*)

BESUGO, PACHAN★   RED BREAM

Gal: ollomol, pancho*   *Por:* goraz, besugo*
Bas: bisigu   *Fre:* dorade, bogaravelle*
Cat: quelet, bogaravell*   *Ger:* Scharfzähner

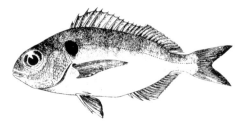

Two species or one? Nowadays, the taxonomists are unanimous in saying 'only one'; but in the past they had two and the pattern of vernacular names certainly fits in with that idea. What seems to be the truth of the matter is that juvenile specimens have blue spots, whereas fully adult ones lack these but have a pronounced dark spot like the one shown above.

I should add that *P cantabricus* appears to be a synonym for what used to be called *P centrodontus*, the fully adult form; and that the latter name has been superseded under the applicable rules by *P bogaraveo*, formerly the name for the juvenile fish (when that was thought to be a separate species) but now for the species as a whole. However, I have an uneasy feeling that if I were writing a taxonomic treatise I would have to give a more complicated explanation!

Anyway: max <> 70, mkt <> 15–50.

The besugo enjoys a high reputation in Spain, where it is consumed in large quantities. In Castilla it is considered to be the classical dish for eating on Nochebuena (Christmas Eve). The Spanish humorist Julio Camba (quoted in my anthology *On Fasting and Feasting*) gave a delightful account of a man disconcerting a party of diners in a restaurant by raising his hat in a gesture of farewell to the fish which they were about to eat: 'an old friend', he explained, which he had been looking at in the window, surrounded by its parsley, every day for some two weeks. Only the besugo would have been suitable as the subject for this little tale!

This species and the pandora (next page) are most suitable for being grilled or baked.

★ The asterisks indicate names applying to the juvenile form.

Family SPARIDAE
Pagellus erythrinus

BRECA   PANDORA

Gal: breca, bica
Bas: lamote
Cat: pagell

Por: bica
Fre: pageot rouge
Ger: Rotbrassen

Max <> 60, mkt <> 10–30. Of a markedly red tint, as the French and German names indicate.

'Carne blanda, delicada y exquisita', says de Juana. When I was living in Tunisia, I rated it a little less highly: 'quite good', suited to baking or grilling.

Pagellus acarne

ALIGOTE   BRONZE BREAM

Gal: pancho picudo, besuguillo
Bas: lentoe, aliota, neskazahar
Cat: besuc

Por: besugo
Fre: pageot blanc
Ger: /

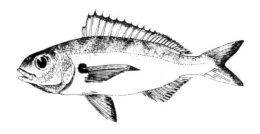

Max <> 35, mkt <> 10–25. A fish which is highly appreciated in Galicia, and indeed elsewhere. Suited to any of the standard treatments for fish of this size.

Sarpa salpa

SALEMA SALEMA

Gal: saboga   *Por:* salema
Bas: sabia   *Fre:* saupe
Cat: salpa   *Ger:* Goldstrieme

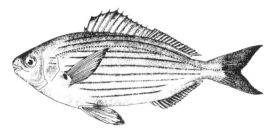

Max <> 50, mkt <> 15–30. The base colour is bluish-grey, with which the 10 or 11 yellow-orange horizontal stripes make a pleasing contrast.

A fish of the East Atlantic and the Mediterranean. Its quality varies according to the mode it is in (migratory or sedentary) and its food. Tunisians, who apparently eat more of it than any other people, have a saying that the salema is at its best during the grape harvest.

Spondyliosoma (formerly Cantharus) cantharus

CHOPA BLACK BREAM

Gal: pancha, ruda, chepa   *Por:* choupa
Bas: ollaka   *Fre:* griset
Cat: càntera   *Ger:* Seekarausche

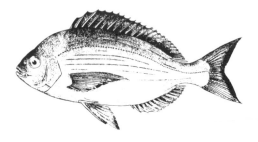

Max <> 60, mkt <> 20–30. A greyish fish with noticeable longitudinal gold stripes, which may be more or less broken. Good eating.

Family CENTRACANTHIDAE
Spicara maena
CHUCLA   PICAREL

Gal: /	*Por:* xucla
Bas: /	*Fre:* mendole commune
Cat: xucla, mena, mata-soldat	*Ger:* Laxierfisch

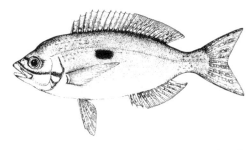

Max <> 25 (male), mkt <> 12–20. This species, its brother shown below on this page, and a couple of other minor species in the family are all too bony to be popular as food; and appreciation of them is confined to rather few localities, eg the island of Korcula in Yugoslavia. In many places the fish bear derogatory names, such as mata-soldat (kill soldier) in some Catalan-speaking areas on either side of the Spanish-French frontier.

Spicara (formerly *Maena*) *smaris*
CARAMEL   PICAREL

Gal: /	*Por:* alcarraz
Bas: /	*Fre:* picarel
Cat: jerret, xula blanca	*Ger:* Pikarel

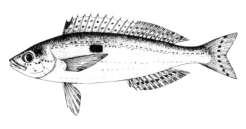

Max <> 20 (male), mkt <> 8–20. Less deep-bodied than the preceding species. Neither of the two is found north of Portugal in the Atlantic.

RED MULLET

The two species of red mullet which inhabit the Mediterranean are regarded by many people as the archetypes of Mediterranean fish, and special to that sea. Such people are surprised to learn that very close relations exist elsewhere, for example in the Indo-Pacific, where they go by the name of goatfish. Indeed some of these goatfish have in the last few decades swum through the Suez Canal into the Mediterranean and established themselves there. (Perhaps one day they will reach the West Mediterranean and Spain, but not for a while yet.)

The name goatfish is given because of the barbels shown in the drawings, which are thought to resemble a goat's beard. It seems like a good name to me, whereas the name red mullet invites confusion with the quite different grey mullet.

The excellence of these fish was recognized in the classical world, and Roman gourmets were willing to pay vast sums (really vast, like $5000 of today's money) for an exceptionally large specimen. A mistake; the largest are not the best.

Family MULLIDAE
Mullus barbatus

SALMONETE DE FANGO RED MULLET

Gal: salmonete de fango
Bas: barbarin, barbadilla,
          izokinkume
Cat: moll de fang

Por: salmonete de vasa
Fre: rouget barbet
Ger: roter Meerbarbe

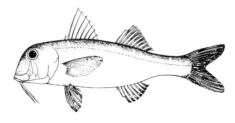

Max <> 30, market <> 10–20. The colour is rosy red all over, although paler underneath.

Mullus surmuletus

SALMONETE DE ROCA

RED MULLET

Gal: salmonete de pedra/de roca
Bas: barbarin, barbadilla, izokinsome
Cat: moll roquer

Por: salmonete
Fre: rouget de roche
Ger: gesteifle Meerbarbe

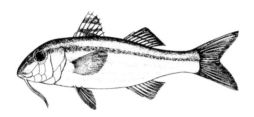

Max <> 40, mkt <> 10–25. This species is distinguished by the three yellowish stripes which run along each side. Like the preceding species, it has quite an extensive range, including the Black Sea, the Mediterranean and much of the East Atlantic.

Red mullet are delicious if grilled over charcoal (in Spain, Salmonetes Asados); but they may also be fried (Salmonetes Fritos) or baked (Salmonetes al Horno).

One interesting version of grilled red mullet in Portugal is Salmonetes Grelhados à Moda do Setúbal, a dish of the fishing port Setúbal. This uses the livers in the sauce, with parsley and lemon juice; and I have heard of a variant in which bitter orange juice is used instead of lemon juice. The liver of the red mullet is counted as a delicacy almost everywhere.

From the cook's point of view, what applies to the first red mullet applies to the second one too – but the latter does tend to be somewhat larger.

GREY MULLET

In case this is not already clear, let me say that it is just a coincidence that red mullet and grey mullet share the word 'mullet' in their English names; they are not closely related to each other.

The grey mullets are larger fish, beautifully streamlined. The family is present in coastal waters and estuaries around the world, and the first species listed here is itself circumglobal in distribution. The small mouths are indicative of feeding habits; the grey mullet feed almost exclusively on organic matter such as seaweeds and, as I have remarked elsewhere, they won much praise from the Roman poet Oppian for 'their gentle and just disposition, harming neither each other nor any other creatures, never staining their lips with blood but in holy fashion feeding always on the green seaweed or mere mud'.

'Or mere mud'; yes, and there lies a problem, for grey mullet which have been grazing on unsalubrious beds of mud have a disagreeable muddy taste. It is well to buy those which come from clean sea water.

The roe of grey mullet is dried and pressed to make the delicacy known as poutargue in France.

Family MUGILIDAE
Mugil cephalus

PARDETE, PARDETÓN   **GREY MULLET**

Gal: muxo   *Por:* taínha olhalvo
Bas: korrokoi bizkarbeitz   *Fre:* mulet cabot
Cat: cap gros, cap plané   *Ger:* Grossköpfige

Max <> 120, mkt <> 30–65. This species is distinguished by the transparent membranes which cover its eyes.

Grey mullet of this and other species may be poached, baked, or fried (a popular method in Portugal). Really good specimens can be grilled.

Liza saliens

GALÚA   LEAPING GREY MULLET

Gal: /
Bas: /
Cat: llisa fusany

Por: taínha
Fre: mulet sauteur
Ger: Springmeeräsche

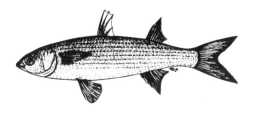

Max <> 40, mkt <> 20–30. Of all the Mediterranean grey mullets this is the one which most noticeably leaps out of the water when escaping from predators.

Liza aurata (formerly *Mugil auratus*)

GALUPE   GOLD GREY MULLET

Gal: muxo
Bas: dabeta korrokoi
Cat: galta-roig

Por: taínha garrento
Fre: mulet doré
Ger: Goldmeeräsche

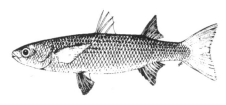

Max <> 55, mkt <> 25–35. There are two golden spots beside each eye; and the sides of the fish have a golden tinge. Those with a strong golden hue have a special Basque name: lerrosain.

Insofar as people distinguish between the species of grey mullet, this counts as a favourite.

I mention here as a footnote that the smallest of the Mediterranean grey mullets is *Odeochilus labeo*; max <> 30. It has few, perhaps no, vernacular names peculiar to it. It is not illustrated.

Liza ramada (= *Mugil capito*)

MORRAGU(E)TE, CAPITON

THIN-LIPPED GREY MULLET

Gal: muxo
Bas: daplata (korrokoi)
Cat: cap pla, llisa

Por: taínha-fataça
Fre: mulet porc
Ger: dünnlippige Meeräsche

Max <> 50, mkt <> 20–35. It is not only in French that this species has a name meaning pig; there is, for example, the name porqua in the Languedoc. Besides thin lips, it has a snout more pointed than most.

Chelon (formerly *Crenimugil*) *labrosus*

LISA

THICK-LIPPED GREY MULLET

Gal: mujel, muxo
Bas: hondoetako korrokoi
Cat: llisera vera, llisa betada

Por: taínha
Fre: mulet lippu
Ger: dicklippige Meeräsche

Max <> 60, mkt <> 20–40. It has a rounder body than other members of the family. Aquaculture of the species takes place in some regions.

WRASSES

A large family, mostly of striking coloration. In many species the two sexes wear different liveries. All the species listed occur in the Mediterranean; few have an Atlantic range as far north as Galicia.

Family LABRIDAE
Labrus bergylta

MARAGOTA WRASSE

Gal: maragota
Bas: durdo
Cat: l

Por: margota
Fre: vieille
Ger: Lippfisch

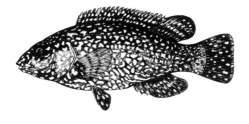

Max <> 60, mkt <> 30–50. The dominant colour is usually green or reddish brown, with pale spots. For cuisine, see the following page.

Labrus bimaculatus (= L mixtus)

GALLANO, GAYANO CUCKOO WRASSE

Gal: rei
Bas: txilibitu
Cat: pastenaga (f), lloro (m)

Por: bodião
Fre: vieille coquette
Ger: bunter Lippfisch

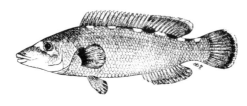

Max <> 40, mkt <> 10–25. A noticeable instance of sexual dichromatism. Females are orange or red, with black spots on the top of the back; males (not shown) are brownish yellow with lots of blue spots.

Labrus merula
MERLO WRASSE

Gal: /
Bas: /
Cat: tort negre
Por: bodião
Fre: merle
Ger: Amsellippfisch

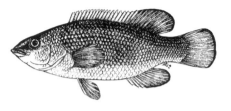

Max <> 45, mkt <> 15–30. Colour varies. Adults may be dark blue, dark green, or brownish, with blue spots on the head.

Labrus viridis (= L turdus)
TORDO, BODIÓN WRASSE VERDE

Gal: /
Bas: /
Cat: grivia
Por: bodião
Fre: labre vert
Ger: grüner Lippfisch

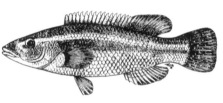

Max <> 45, mkt <> 15–35. The colour of the body is generally green.

Thalassoma pavo
PEZ VERDE ORNATE WRASSE

Gal: /
Bas: /
Cat: fredí
Por: peixe verde
Fre: girelle paon
Ger: Meerpfau

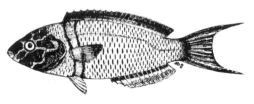

Max <> 25, mkt <> 10–20. Young specimens and females (not shown) have a greenish brown body with five broad blue vertical bands; males have a dark red head 'netted' with blue, and a single vertical blue band just behind the pectoral fin.

Coris julis

Julia, Doncella   Rainbow Wrasse

Gal: doncella, xulia
Bas: dontzeila, palabeltza
Cat: donzella
Por: peixe-rey
Fre: girelle
Ger: Meerjunker

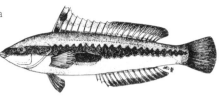

Max <> 25, mkt <> 10–20. A male is shown, with its typical red or orange band, often bordered with light blue, running along the side in a curious pattern.

A good fish for fish soups.

Symphodus (formerly *Crenilabrus*) *tinca*

Señorita, Peto   Peacock Wrasse

Gal: /
Bas: txilibitu
Cat: tort, satx, rossignol
Por: bodião
Fre: crénilabre paon
Ger: Pfauenlippfisch

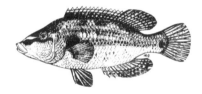

Max <> 40 or more, mkt <> 10–25. A pretty little fish which has numerous close relations in its genus, of which several others are large enough to be of gastronomic interest and are listed briefly on the next page.

Symphodus roissali (= *S quinquemaculatus*)

Tordo   Five-Spotted Wrasse

Gal: /
Bas: karraspio
Cat: tort, roqué vert
Por: bodião
Fre: crénilabre à cinq tâches
Ger: fünffleckiger Lippfisch

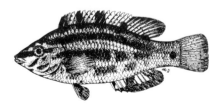

Max <> 17, mkt <> 8–12.

Porredana
Symphodus (= Crenilabrus) melops
Gal: vello, serrán
Cat: tort roquer
Por: bodião

Max <> 28, mkt <> 10–20.
Known as corkwing in English.

Magnote, Bodión
Symphodus (= Crenilabrus) cinereus
Gal: vello, serran
Por: bodião

Max <> 16, mkt <> 7–10.

Tordo de Roca
Symphodus (= Crenilabrus) mediterraneus
Cat: tort, canari, porcellana
Por: bodião

Max <> 17, mkt <> 8–12.

Tordo Picudo
Symphodus rostratus
Cat: grivieta, doncellete, petarch
Por: /

Max <> 13, mkt <> 5–8.

At this point we have got down to very small members of the wrasse family. De Juana and de Juana (1987) observe that there are others too, such as *Symphodus ocellatus* and *S doederleini*, which have a max <> of about 10 and are sold as 'morralla'. Any of these wrasses might be 'karraspio' in Basque.

However, we still have to note an Atlantic species, found also in the Mediterranean, the **goldsinny**:

Grivieta
Ctenolabrus rupestris
Gal: vello, serrán
Por: bodião, rei

Max <> 18, mkt <> 10–12.

Xyrichthys novacula

RAOR   CLEAVER WRASSE

Gal: /   *Por: mordedor*
Bas: /   *Fre: rason*
Cat: raó, roso   *Ger: /*

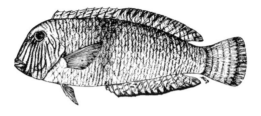

A thin pinkish fish, max <> 30, mkt <> 20. Popular in Majorca from late August to mid October. It is found in other parts of the Mediterranean also, and to some extent in the Atlantic. Alternative Portuguese names include elefante and coelho da costa. Other Spanish names are: pinta, papgalo, galán.

Family SCARIDAE
Sparisoma (= Euscarus) cretense

VIEJA COLORADA   PARROTFISH

Gal: /   *Por: papagaio*
Bas: /   *Fre: perroquet-vieillard*
Cat: /   *Ger: /*

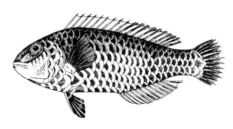

Max <> 50, mkt <> 10–30. Supposedly found in most parts of the Mediterranean, and in the Atlantic from Senegal to Portugal; but in reality seems to occur mainly in the East Mediterranean and around Madeira, the Canaries, etc. A good fish, greatly prized in classical Rome.

A MIXED CATCH OF MORE
PERCIFORM FISH

Here we come to the little sand-eel, followed by the tribe of weevers, a hazard to barefoot bathers, and then the villainous-looking scabbard fish.

This last is a particularly interesting fish, partly because it makes much better eating than people who have not met it might suppose, and partly because it looms so large in the markets of Portugal and Madeira. Its habits and distribution are such that it falls to Portuguese fishermen to make the largest catches, and what they land is greatly appreciated. The silver scabbard fish is considered to be 'more elegant', a Portuguese friend tells me, because of its colour; but the black one is just as good.

Family AMMODYTIDAE
Ammodytes tobianus

AGUACIOSO, BARRINAIRE

SAND-EEL

Gal: bolo	*Por:* sandilho, galeota
Bas: abisoi	*Fre:* équille
Cat: /	*Ger:* Sandaal, Sandspierling

Max <> 20, mkt <> 10–15. Sand-eels are all inshore fish, with a capability of burrowing into the sand. Of the various members of the family, *Ammodytes tobianus* (above) is an Atlantic fish. So is *Hyperoplus lanceolatus* (below left), which is a larger fish (max <> 35); the Spanish name for it is **pion**; and it may be called bolo or anguiacho in Galicia.

On the other hand, the slightly smaller *Gymnammodytes cicerellus* (below right) is more usual in the Mediterranean, especially (so far as Spain is concerned) in Catalonian waters. It is **barrinaire,** or sonsu in Catalan.

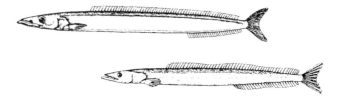

Trachinus draco

ESCORPIÓN, ARAÑA BLANCA

WEEVER

Gal: peixe araña, escorpión
de altura
Bas: xabiroi, lasun-arrain
Cat: aranya blanca

Por: aranha grande
Fre: vive
Ger: Petermännchen

Max <> 45, mkt <> 10–30. Sometimes called the 'greater weever', not because it is the largest, but in relation to the 'lesser weever', *Echiichthys vipera* (not shown), also **escorpión** in Spanish, escorpión da praia in Galician.

Weevers are generally relegated to bouillabaisse or other fish soups or stews, and it is only the large specimens which are suited to other treatment. But the large ones produce fine fillets which can be cooked in any of the regular ways.

Be sure that the venomous dorsal spines have been cut off when you buy them.

Trachinus radiatus

VIBORA

WEEVER

Gal: /
Bas: /
Cat: aranya de cap negre

Por: (peixe) aranha
Fre: vive rayée
Ger: /

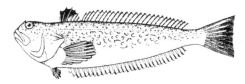

Max <> 50, mkt <> 10–30. Yellowish, with brown marks which form a distinctive pattern along the sides.

Family TRACHINIDAE

Trachinus araneus

ARAÑA   WEEVER

Gal: /
Bas: /
Cat: aranya fragata

Por: (peixe) aranha
Fre: vive araignée
Ger: /

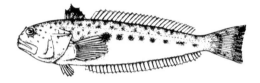

Max <> 50, mkt <> 20–30. This species ventures no further north than Portugal in the Atlantic, but like the others it is present throughout the Mediterranean.

Family URANOSCOPIDAE

Uranoscopus scaber

RATA, MIRACIELO   STAR-GAZER

Gal: /
Bas: /
Cat: saltabardissa

Por: papatabaco
Fre: boeuf
Ger: Stemguker

Max <> 35, mkt <> 15–30. The eyes are set to point permanently upwards and the mouth is designed to provide the maximum reception area for whatever prey incautiously passes over it. Like the weevers, this fish has a strategy which calls for it to be half buried and almost invisible in the sand, where it awaits its food.

For the cook, the star-gazer is like one more weever, neither better nor worse.

Family T R I C H I U R I D A E

Lepidopus caudatus

PEZ CINTO   SCABBARD FISH

Gal: sable
Bas: ezpata-arrain
Cat: sable

Por: peixe espada
Fre: sabre
Ger: Degenfisch

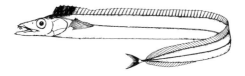

Max <> 210, mkt <> 50–150. The silver body is without scales. Range covers the whole western basin of the Mediterranean, and the East Atlantic as far north as Galicia.

I enjoyed this fish so many times in Tunisia that it counts as one of my favourites in the Mediterranean area. The rear end, admittedly, tapers off so much that it offers little to eat; but sections cut from amidships or further forward are just right for being pan-fried.

Aphanopus carbo

PEZ CINTO,   BLACK SCABBARD
PEZ SABLE   FISH

Gal: sable negro
Bas: ezpata-arrain
Cat: /

Por: espada preta
Fre: sabre
Ger: schwarzer Degenfisch

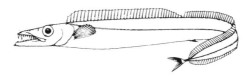

Max <> 110, mkt <> 50–80. A coppery-black fish with iridescent tints. Range from Iceland down to Madeira (where it dominates the local catch) and elsewhere in the East Atlantic and in other oceans too.

Cuisine: as for the larger scabbard fish above.

THE MACKEREL AND TUNA FAMILY

This is the most important single family of what Spaniards call 'blue fish' (pescado azul, see page 13). It includes fish which are relatively small, like the ordinary Atlantic mackerel of the Mediterranean and the Atlantic, but also very large fish such as bluefin tuna. They all have features in common, for example a beautifully streamlined shape which suits their way of life (endlessly swimming at high speed across the high seas); and they all have a relatively high oil content.

Those, like myself, who find mackerel delicious are puzzled by the lack of enthusiasm for it at other times (in classical Greece and Rome) and in some places at the present time, for example, Spain; in Galicia, the catch is usually relegated to the canneries. And it is significant that some of the names given to the innocent mackerel can be used in a way which implies dislike for its appearance (e g maquereau in French means pimp).

However, although the mackerel is disdained, the tuna is held in very high esteem. The seasonal migrations of these big fish along the coast make them vulnerable to capture in specially constructed tuna traps (almadrabas). There used to be some on Spain's Mediterranean coast, but no more. Nowadays, the most famous and most productive ones are on the Atlantic coast, from the south of Portugal to the Strait of Gibraltar. Indeed this area, centred on Cadiz, is known as 'El Mar de Atun'. Exploitation of the tuna in this region dates back to Phoenician times.

The learned author Arbex has many interesting things to say about the pejorative connotations on land of words derived from 'tuna'; thus 'tunante' means 'vagabond, villain, scamp', and 'tuna' itself refers to the life of such people or to a group of black-cloaked students who go round making music and roistering. It seems that in the past all sorts of vagrants or dubious characters were attracted to the almadrabas in search of a quick profit and the company of other rascals. Cervantes himself described the almadrabas as an 'academy for rogues' where a budding rogue must pass at least two seasons before graduating.

Records of tuna catches go back a long way. José Carlos de Luna, drawing on the archives of the Dukes of Medina Sidonia (at Sanlucar de Barrameda) states that in the year 1588 the number of tuna taken at Conil and Zahara alone was 110,152. In more recent times, in a record year in the 1920s, over 100,000 tuna in all were taken.

The catch has for some time been declining, but is still very large. Much of it goes to Japanese buyers who are unfailingly in attendance, pocket calculators poised in their hands, as the tuna are auctioned. It is a relief to the Spaniards that the Japanese depart without the tuna eggs or milt, both of which are delicacies for Spanish palates.

The pressed and dried eggs (Huevas de Atun) may be served in tapas bars.

Family SCOMBRIDAE
Scomber scombrus

CABALLA   MACKEREL

Gal: xarda; perrilla,
tomo (small ones)
Bas: berdel, makael
Cat: verat

Por: sarda
Fre: maquereau
Ger: Makrele

Max <> 50, mkt <> 18–30. The dark blue back merges into green sides with dark blue wavy lines running down.

As already mentioned, Spaniards are not enthusiastic about mackerel. However, there certainly are some recipes, including the preparation of the fish 'en escabeche' and cooking them with lots of tomatoes (the acidity of which 'cuts' the oiliness). In Galicia, Caballa al limó is a standard preparation.

Scomber japonicus

ESTORNINO   CHUB MACKEREL

Gal: xarda pintada, verdel
Bas: begi aundi
Cat: bis

Por: cavala
Fre: maquereau espagnol
Ger: Kolias

Max <> 50, mkt <> 15–30. Note the pattern on the upper sides and the more curved line of the belly.

Sarda sarda

BONITO BONITO

Gal: bonito del sur
Bas: albokera, atun txiki
Cat: bonítol

Por: serra, bonito
Fre: bonite à dos rayé
Ger: Pelamide

Max <> 90, mkt <> 25–65. A famously good fish.

Spanish recipes for 'bonito' may refer to this species or (in the north) to *Thunnus alalunga* (page 90). Two dishes, Bonito en Escabeche (fried, then marinated in vinegar with garlic and bay leaf) and Bonito al Horno (baked with potato, tomato, onion) are well known.

Orcynopsis unicolor

TASARTE BONITO

Gal: /
Bas: /
Cat: /

Por: palometa
Fre: palomète
Ger: /

Max <> 110, mkt <> 25–50. A Mediterranean species, relatively uncommon (even along the North African coast, its preferred haunt), but very good to eat.

Thunnus thynnus

ATÚN TUNA

Gal: atún (rojo), cimarrón
Bas: atun gorri, egalabur, zimarroi
Cat: tonyina

Por: rabilho
Fre: thon rouge
Ger: grosser Thun

Max <> 300, mkt <> 50–150. This Mediterranean and Atlantic species is correctly called *Thunnus thynnus thynnus*, to distinguish it from its brother sub-species in the Pacific, *T t orientalis*.

There is another Atlantic species, shown in the drawing at the foot of the page, which is *T obesus*, the big-eye tuna. It is present off the west coast of the Iberian peninsula, and often taken in the vicinity of Madeira and the Azores. The Spanish and Portuguese names are **patudo**.

In addition, there is *T albacares*, the yellowfin tuna, which is also often caught off the Canaries, the Azores and Madeira. Its Spanish name is **rabil**, and its meat may be sold as 'atún claro'. It is not shown, but may be recognized by its bright yellow dorsal and anal fins and finlets.

Tuna meat is rich, substantial, dark red. Grilled steaks are a favourite way of preparing it; or thicker pieces can be braised or stewed with wine, vegetables and other flavourings. Empanadillas de Atún (tuna pasties) are very popular throughout Spain.

Tuna meat from the back of the fish, which has been dried and salted, becoming very hard and dense and rather like certain cured hams, is a Spanish delicacy known as mojama.

Thunnus alalunga

ALBACORA, BONITO DEL NORTE

ALBACORE

Gal: bonito del norte, atún blanco
Bas: hegaluze, atun zuri
Cat: bacora

Por: voador
Fre: germon
Ger: weisser Thun

Max <> 100, mkt <> 50–80. (The fact that this tuna is called 'albacora' in Spanish and 'albacore' in English might make one think that it is the same as the species *T albacora*. Not so! See the preceding page for this other species, which only rarely visits the mainlands of Spain and Portugal.)

The meat is lighter in colour and fat content than that of *T thynnus*, and preferred by some.

Euthynnus alletteratus
(= *E quadripunctatus*)

BACORETA

LITTLE TUNNY

Gal: albacora
Bas: ami, atun txiki, xarmota
Cat: tonyina

Por: alvacora
Fre: thonine
Ger: Thonine

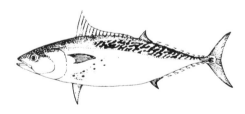

Max <> 100, mkt <> 30–80. Found throughout the Mediterranean and on both sides of the Atlantic, but not common as far north as Galicia.

Katsuwonus pelamis

LISTADO, ALISTADO   SKIPJACK

Gal: alistado, bonito raiado
Bas: ami
Cat: ratllat, palomida

Por: corrinelo
Fre: bonite à ventre rayé
Ger: echte Bonito

Max <> 100, mkt <> 30–80. Note the dark stripes running along the lower part of its side. A common fish in the Atlantic and Pacific (it is the Japanese 'katsuwo'), less common in the Mediterranean.

Auxis rochei (formerly *A thazard*)

MELVA   FRIGATE MACKEREL

Gal: zurdo
Bas: /
Cat: melv(er)a

Por: judeu
Fre: melva
Ger: unechter Bonito

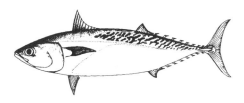

Max <> 50, mkt <> 20–40. A fish which is found all round the world in warm waters, but uncommon as far north as Galicia.

Given its size, this species ranks with the true mackerels (*Scomber* spp, page 87) for culinary purposes. The dried flesh is served as an appetizer and the dried roe is an expensive delicacy in Murcia.

Xiphias gladius

PEZ ESPADA   SWORDFISH

Gal: peixe espada
Bas: ezpatarrain, txitxi-ezpata
Cat: emperador, peix espasa

Por: espadarte, agulhão
Fre: espadon
Ger: Schwertfisch

Max <> 450, mkt <> 80–220. A fish of global distribution and reputation. It is clear that the design of the swordfish is an efficacious one; otherwise it would not have survived and be present all round the world. And it is clear that the (literally) salient feature of the design is the 'sword'. But no one seems to be quite sure what the purpose of the sword is. The idea once entertained that it was a weapon which enabled these fish to attack and even to sink boats was wrong (there have been a few instances of the broken-off sword of a swordfish being found stuck through the wooden bottom of a small boat, but no evidence of deliberate attacks). A more plausible theory is that the swordfish can flail its sword about in a school of smaller fish, stunning scores of them at a time and being then able to eat them up. But ... no one seems to know for sure.

Although the swordfish is definitely in the category of 'pescado azul' (page 10), its fat content is relatively low, much lower than the tuna, for example. If one is grilling fairly thin swordfish steaks, there is a risk of their becoming too dry.

Aguilas in the south of Murcia in Spain used to be an important fishing port for swordfish; but few large ones are taken nowadays.

NOTE: in Madeira and possibly in some parts of mainland Portugal, peixe espada may refer to the sawfish, *Pristis cuspidatus*.

Stromateus fiatola
PÁMPANO   POMFRET

Gal: /
Bas: /
Cat: pudenta
Por: pamplo
Fre: fiatole
Ger: /

Max <> 50, mkt <> 20–35. Quite a pretty fish, thin and deep-bodied, bearing dark spots on a bluish or brownish back, and with a whitish belly.

Because of its shape, the pomfret can be treated like flatfish; but it is of only medium quality.

Parablennius (formerly *Blennius*) *gattorugine*
CABRUZA   (ROCK) BLENNY

Gal: lorchos (general name)   *Por:* marachomba
Bas: kabuxa (general name)   *Fre:* baveuse
                          Cat: /   *Ger:* Schleimfisch

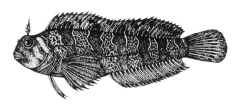

Max <> 35, mkt <> 20. Among the largest of the two dozen or so blennies in Spanish and Portuguese waters. Its coloration provides it with good camouflage, aided by a fleshy little 'tree' growing on the top of its head.

The butterfly blenny (Spanish **torillo**) has a very large, sail-like, dorsal fin.

Centrolophus niger

ROMERILLO, MORO NEGRO

BLACKFISH

Gal: pampano negro
Bas: zentrolofo beltz
Cat: pampól

Por: liro, pescada preta
Fre: centrolophe noir
Ger: /

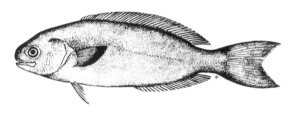

Max <> 150, mkt <> 60–90. The colour is not really 'black' as in many of the vernacular names, but ranges from russet through chocolate to blackish blue. This dark and solitary fish, which only rarely forms schools, frequents deeper waters. Not very much is known about it. But it has excellent white flesh and is well worth buying when it appears in the market. So far as I can tell, it is met more often off the coast near Cadiz, and in the waters near the Azores and Madeira, than elsewhere; but it is certainly known in parts of the West Mediterranean.

All standard methods of preparation suit this fish.

Family GOBIIDAE

Gobius niger jozo

CHAPARRUDO, GOBIO (NEGRO)

(BLACK) GOBY

Gal: lorcha, lorcho
Bas: zarbo (beltz)
Cat: cabot, gobit

Por: caboz
Fre: gobie (noire)
Ger: Grundel, Schwarzgrundel

One of the most common of more than 50 gobies which frequent the Mediterranean and adjacent waters of the Atlantic. The black goby is one of the few which attains a respectable size (up to 20 cm) and it is not uncommon in the markets, although more common in Turkey and Italy than elsewhere.

Other species of goby are:
G paganellus (Spanish **paganel** or **bobi**)
G cobitis (Spanish **cabezudo**)
G cruentatus (Spanish **gobio de boca roja**)

In a closely related genus we find a similar little fish, *Aphia minuta*, which is quite well known in Spain as **chanquete** (Catalan, xanguet or jonquet) and in the south of France as nounat or nonnat. In English it is the transparent goby, a name which refers to its almost total lack of colour (not the same thing as being transparent, but it gives the right idea).

The chanquete used to be especially well known in Málaga, where it was a famous dish, crisply fried and eaten more or less by the spoonful. For some time, however, and for good reasons, it has been forbidden to fish for or market this species.

MAILY-CHEEKED FISH

The families of scorpion fish (Scorpaenidae) and gurnards (Triglidae) share the unusual characteristic of having what might be called 'armour-plated cheeks'; and, one might add, big heads.

The former used to be mainly known as fish essential to a genuine Provençal bouillabaisse (which is, however, a somewhat bogus concept, as I have shown elsewhere). Their uncouth appearance was thought to disqualify them for other and more refined purposes. Now, however, they are recognized as fine fish in their own right; and 'filets de rascasse' have become fashionable in France.

In Spain the most famous dish of scorpion fish is Pastel de Cabracho, a sort of coarse mousse of the flesh of this fish, associated especially with Santander and Bilbao.

Family SCORPAENIDAE

Scorpaena scrofa

CABRACHO   SCORPION FISH

Gal: escarapote da petra
Bas: krabarroka
Cat: cap roig, polla de mar

Por: rainúnculo
Fre: rascasse rouge
Ger: roter Drachenkopf

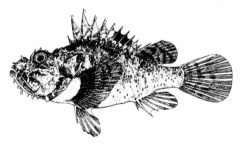

Max <> 65, mkt <> 20–30. The largest and most handsome member of the family. It is well known throughout the Mediterranean, but also ranges from the English Channel down to Senegal in the Atlantic.

Baking a whole specimen is recommended. Otherwise fillets can be cut off and cooked as you please.

Family SCORPAENIDAE
Scorpaena porcus

RASCACIO   **SCORPION FISH**

Gal: escarapote
Bas: krabarroka ertain
Cat: escórpora

Por: rascasso
Fre: rascasse noire
Ger: braunner Drachenkpof

Max <> 30, mkt <> 10–20. A smaller species, which has a range similar to *S scrofa*. It may easily be confused with another and still smaller species, *S maderensis* (Spanish, **rascacio de Madeira**) which is found on the Mediterranean coast of Spain.

Scorpaena elongata

GALLINETA ROSADA   **(SLENDER ROCKFISH)**

Gal /
Bas: /
Cat: /

Por: rascasso
Fre: rascasse rose
Ger: /

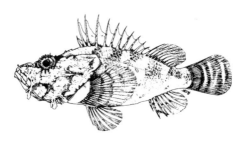

Max <> 55, mkt <> 20–40. A species of the West Mediterranean and Morocco, of a noticeably rosy colour.

Scorpaena notata (formerly *S ustulata*)

ESCÓRPORA   SMALL SCORPION FISH

Gal: escarapote da fango
Bas: krabarroka txiki
Cat: rasclot, cap tinyós

Por: rascasso
Fre: petite rascasse
Ger: kleiner roter Dranchenkopf

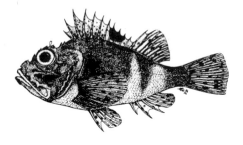

Max <> 24, mkt <> 10–15. Reddish brown, relatively small, quite easily confused with small specimens of the larger species (or of various other, obscure, small species).

Helicolenus dactylopterus

GALLINETA   BLUEMOUTH

Gal: cabra da altura
Bas: sakoneko krabarroka
Cat: panegall

Por: cantarilho
Fre: rascasse de fond
Ger: Blaumaul

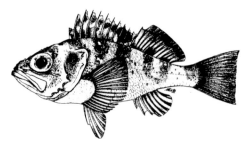

Max <> 45, mkt <> 30. The mouth is of a leaden blue colour inside; hence the English name and an alternative Spanish name, boca negra (another is cabra de hondura, goat of the deep, like the Galician name). A close relation of the rascasses (above and preceding page) but, for culinary purposes, closer still to the redfish and 'Norway haddock' of the North Atlantic (*Sebastes* spp).

Trigla lucerna
BEJEL   TUB GURNARD

Gal: alfóndiga
Bas: perloi handi
Cat: luerna

Por: cabrinha
Fre: grondin perlon, galinette
Ger: roter Knurrhahn

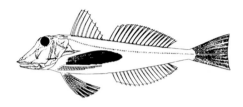

Max <> 73 (corresponding to a weight of 6 kg), mkt <> 20–40. The back is usually of a yellowish or greyish rose colour. The pectoral fins (red with peacock-blue and green spots and margins) provide an instant recognition point.

Gurnards vary in size and quality and have a family tendency to be dry. The bigger and better ones make a good dish if cooked with added oil or moisture, while others slip readily into, and help to flavour, fish soups. The tub gurnard is the largest and one of the best.

Trigla lyra
GARNEO   PIPER

Gal: escacho de altura
Bas: perloi lira
Cat: garneu

Por: cabra
Fre: grondin lyre
Ger: Pfeifenfisch

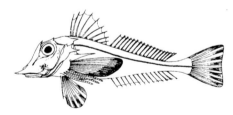

Max <> 60, mkt <> 20–40. Red above, pale below. Incidentally, the fact that most gurnards have red or reddish backs results in there being a general Basque name, arraingorri, which simply means 'red fish' and may be applied to any such.

Eutrigla gurnardus

BORRACHO, PERLON   GREY GURNARD

Gal: crego   *Por:* cabra morena
Bas: perloi beltz   *Fre:* grondin gris
Cat: lluerna verde   *Ger:* grauer Knurrhahn

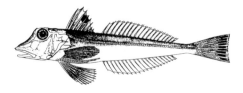

Max <> 60, mkt <> 15–40. Generally of a grey colour, but it may be brownish and with tints of red above.

Trigloporus lastoviza

RUBIO, BORRACHO   STREAKED GURNARD

Gal: escacho, rubio   *Por:* cabra
Bas: perloi zirrindatu   *Fre:* grondin (rouge)
Cat: borratxo, rafalet   *Ger:* gestreifter Knurrhaan

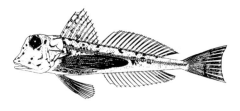

Max <> 40, mkt <> 15. This species has an extensive range in the East Atlantic as well as in the Mediterranean. The diagonal markings caused it to be named (formerly) *Trigla lineata*.

The Spanish name borracho, echoed in the Catalan name borratxo, means drunkard, presumably referring to the red colour which is characteristic both of this fish and of a drunkard's nose.

I think it was this species which was so beautifully cooked for us in a sauce of fresh tomatoes by the captain of a Tunisian trawler.

Family TRIGLIDAE
Aspitrigla cuculus

ARETE **RED GURNARD**

Gal: escacho bravo
Bas: perloi kuku
Cat: gallineta

Por: bobo
Fre: grondin rouge
Ger: Seekuckuck

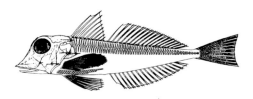

Max <> 50 (so one of the larger gurnards), mkt <> 20–25. This is one of the gurnards which have a bright red back; hence the English name.

This species and the one below both have a wide range in the Mediterranean and East Atlantic.

Aspitrigla obscura

ARETE ALETÓN, **LONGFIN GURNARD**
ARETE OSCURO

Gal: escacho, rubio
Bas: perloi ilun
Cat: /

Por: cabra
Fre: grondin sombre
Ger: /

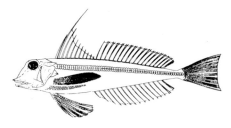

A similar species, but smaller (max <> 35, mkt <> 15–20) and of rather sombre coloration.

Family TRIGLIDAE
Lepidotrigla cavillone

CABETE   LARGE-SCALED GURNARD

Gal: /   *Por:* ruivo
Bas: /   *Fre:* cavillone
Cat: clavilló, cabet de escata,   *Ger:* /
pelut de escata

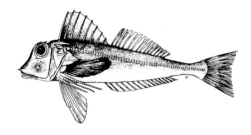

Max <> 20, mkt <> 12. This gurnard has a reddish back and pale underside. Its range does not extend further north than Portugal. Of scant commercial importance.

Lepidotrigla dieuzeide, named after one of the three French authors of an excellent study of fish in Algerian waters, is similar in appearance and size.

Family PERISTEDIIDAE
Peristedion cataphractum

ARMADO   ARMED GURNARD

Gal: malarmado   *Por:* bergela
Bas: /   *Fre:* malarmat
Cat: malarmat, armat   *Ger:* Panzerhahn

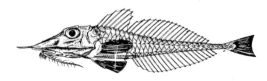

Max <> 40, mkt <> 10–25. This species differs from those in the family Triglidae in having an 'armour plate' of scutes (as opposed to scales) over its body, plus a forked snout and a couple of straggly barbels.

FLATFISH AND SOME ODDITIES

Flatfish are adapted to lying flat on their side on the sea bed. The coloration of their backs usually blends with this environment.

Both eyes of a flatfish are on the same 'side'; sometimes the left-hand side, in which case they are 'sinistral' flatfish, otherwise on the right-hand side, which makes them 'dextral'. Drawings of the two sorts must therefore face different ways on the page; otherwise the artist would be showing an impossibility.

The catalogue of flatfish begins with the sinistral species and then comes to the dextral ones. The latter include all the fish correctly called 'soles'.

Flatfish, because of their shape, are suitable for frying, poaching, or grilling. This last treatment should be reserved for flatfish of good quality and firm flesh (the so-called 'Dover sole', page 111, is the outstanding example). The largest flatfish, such as the turbot (next page) will yield steaks; but filleting is usually the best technique to follow with flatfish which are not being presented whole.

Family SCOPHTHALMIDAE

Scophthalmus rhombus

RÉMOL   BRILL

Gal: curuxo, sollo
Bas: erreboilo ezkatadun
Cat: rémol

Por: rodovalho
Fre: barbue
Ger: Glattbutt

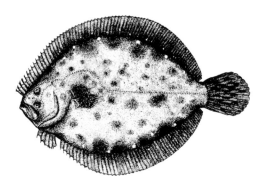

Max <> 75, mkt <> 25–45. Esteemed in Galicia and elsewhere, but not as much as the turbot (next page).

Psetta maxima

RODABALLO TURBOT

Gal: rodaballo, rodo (small)   *Por:* parracho
Bas: erreboilo arrunt   *Fre:* turbot
Cat: rémol de petxines   *Ger:* Steinbutt

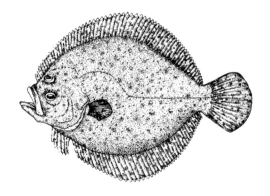

Max <> 100, mkt <> 40–65. The colour varies according to that of the bottom on which the fish finds itself; usually greyish or brown or reddish-brown.

A fish of very high quality which is, for example, the most expensive fish in Galicia.

Rodaballo a la Sidra, cooked in the oven, is well liked in the northern, cider-producing, regions of Spain. Rodaballo al Txakolí con Pimientos is a popular Basque dish.

Phrynorhombus regius

PELAYA MISERES ECKSTROM'S TOPKNOT

A much smaller member of the same family; max <> 20. Brownish in colour and prettily marked.

The Portuguese name is bruxa.

Lepidorhombus whiffiagonis

GALLO   MEGRIM

Gal: meiga (macho), rapante
Bas: oilar handi
Cat: pelaia bruixa, capellá

Por: areeiro
Fre: cardine (franche)
Ger: /

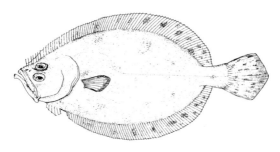

Max <> 60, mkt <> around 30. Found in the West Mediterranean and widely in the East Atlantic.

A fish which is rated quite highly by cooks. Small ones may be pan-fried (Gallos Pequeños Fritos) and larger ones yield good fillets.

Lepidorhombus boscii

GALLO   (FOUR-SPOTTED) MEGRIM

Gal: meiga (femia), rapante
Bas: oilar txiki
Cat: pelaia bruixa, capellá

Por: areeiro
Fre: cardine (à quatre tâches)
Ger: /

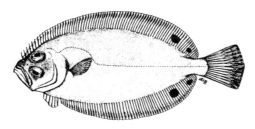

A smaller relation; max <> 40, mkt <> 25–30. Dorsal and anal fins each bear two black spots near the tail.

Cuisine: as for the larger species above.

Citharus linguatula (formerly *C macrolepidotus*)

SOLLETA SPOTTED FLOUNDER

Gal: /
Bas: /
Cat: pelaia (rosa), capellá

Por: carta de bico
Fre: feuille
Ger: /

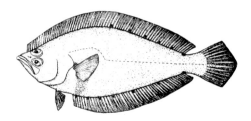

Max <> 30, mkt <> 20. Unusual among flatfish in having a spiny ray at the front of its pelvic fin.

Family BOTHIDAE

Bothus podas

PODÁS, ROMBO WIDE-EYED
DE ARENA FLOUNDER

Gal: /
Bas: /
Cat: puput

Por: carta
Fre: rombou podas
Ger: augenfleckiger Steinbutt

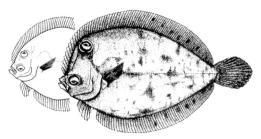

Max <> 25, mkt <> 10–12. Note how widely spaced the eyes are (the main drawing shows a male; the spacing is less marked in the female, as shown in the subsidiary drawing on the left).

Family BOTHIDAE
Arnoglossus laterna
PELUDA   SCALDFISH

Gal: rapapelos, rapante   *Por:* areeiro
Bas: oilar eskuin   *Fre:* fausse limande
Cat: pelaia (rosa)   *Ger:* Lammzunge

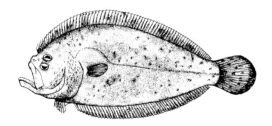

Max <> 20, mkt <> 8–15. The back is an uneven brown in colour; and the scales and skin rub off easily, hence 'scaldfish'.

A thori (below left) is slightly larger (max <> 25), but has the diminutive name **peludilla** in Spanish. Note the more symmetrical shape of the body, and the elongated second ray of the dorsal fin.

A imperialis (below right), **peluda** in Spanish, is also slightly larger and the male of this species (unlike the female) sports a number of elongated rays of the dorsal fin – about five, starting with the second.

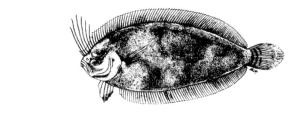

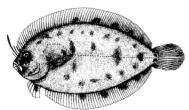

Pleuronectes platessa

PLATIJA, SOLLA   PLAICE

Gal: solla de altura   *Por:* solha
Bas: platuxa   *Fre:* plie
Cat: palaia   *Ger:* Scholle

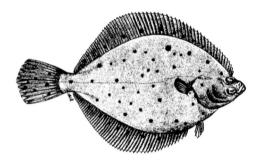

Max <> 90, mkt <> 30–40. A species of the East Atlantic, found also in the West Mediterranean. The pretty markings, orange spots on a brown back, are a familiar sight in European fish shops and markets, but appreciation of this fish varies from region to region. The Portuguese think highly of it (as do the Danes, for example, further north), but its standing in northern Spain is less high. Galicians prefer the flounder (opposite).

Plaice marketed in the north of Spain may well have been caught in waters to the south of Ireland. It is worth mentioning here that from these same waters may come catches of a very much larger flatfish, the halibut, *Hippoglossus hippoglossus*, Spanish **fletan,** whose range extends from the Bay of Biscay up to Greenland and Spitsbergen. A single specimen may weigh up to 300 kg, so this fish completely outclasses in size any flat-fish present in Spanish and Portuguese waters. The most recent information available from the Casa de las Ciencias in La Coruña is that there are still only isolated examples of halibut appearing in the fish auctions at Galician ports.

Platichthys flesus

PLATIJA, PLATUSA (EUROPEAN) FLOUNDER

Gal: solla, platixa
Bas: platuxa latz
Cat: plana, rémol de riu

Por: solha da pedras*
Fre: flet
Ger: Flunder

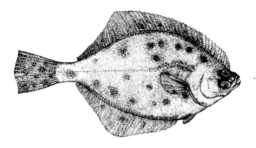

Max <> 50, mkt <> 10–30. Of two sub-species, it is *P flesus flesus* which is found in the West Mediterranean and East Atlantic.

This species is abundant in Galician waters and is highly appreciated. In Galicia and some other parts of Spain the name solla may be applied to it, although it belongs more correctly to the plaice.

A curious feature of this flounder is that, while it is one of the dextral (right side up) flatfish, it may occur in reversed form (sinistral, left side up). Anyone meeting a reversed specimen in a market could easily be puzzled by this. It would be even more astonishing to meet an albino flounder, such as was once captured in England: white on both sides, with pink eyes and fins, a pretty sight.

The flounder can and does enter brackish and fresh waters, especially in the summer. This accounts for the second of the Catalan names shown above, referring to its presence in rivers. It seems, however, not to have been noticed often in Iberian mainland rivers, although definitely reported in the Ebro.

General remarks (page 103) about cooking flatfish apply to this and the preceding species. Bear in mind that, over the whole of its extensive range ('from the White Sea to the Black Sea'), it is possible to find quite different opinions about its quality. On the assumption that these represent differences in the fish rather than in the human beings who eat them the natural inference is that the flounders of Iberian waters are about the best one can have.

* Many other Portuguese names include azevia, dorminhoca, patruça, patusca, petisca, solhão and solho.

Buglossidium luteum (formerly *Solea lutea*)

TAMBOR SOLENETTE

Gal: I
Bas: lenguana
Cat: golleta

Por: lingua de gato
Fre: petite sole jaune
Ger: Zwergzunge

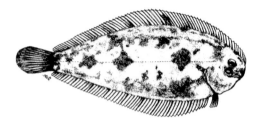

A small sole: max <> 15, mkt <> 6–10. The quality is good.

Dicologoglossa cuneata

ACEDÍA WEDGE SOLE

Gal: I
Bas: lengoradu buruhandi
Cat: I

Por: lingua, asvião
Fre: céteau
Ger: I

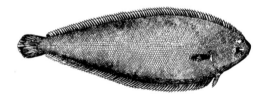

Max <> 30, mkt <> 10–20. A species which belongs to the East Atlantic and comes only a short way into the West Mediterranean. The name lenguadillo is sometimes used in the region of Málaga.

The acedías from the mouth of the Guadalquivir (Sanlucar and Chipiona) are famous for their fine delicate flesh and even preferred by local people to *Solea vulgaris* (next page). General Primo de Rivera, when ruling the country before the Republic of 1931, had acedías (just dipped in boiling oil, then packed in a sandwich box) sent to him daily from Jerez de la Frontera by the night train to Madrid.

Solea vulgaris

LENGUADO SOLE

Gal: lenguado, lirpa (small)   *Por:* linguado
Bas: lenguan, bilau, mihiarrain   *Fre:* sole
Cat: llenguado   *Ger:* Seezunge

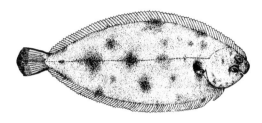

Max <> 70, mkt <> 15–45. This is the famous 'Dover sole', so called because the port of Dover used to be the chief source of supply to London; in fact its range extends far to the north and south of Dover and right through the Mediterranean.

A fish of superb quality, whose firm white flesh, with its delicate flavour, has made it the favourite of chefs. Best grilled or pan-fried; but the fillets can be lifted and subjected to any honorific culinary treatment.

I am told that in the Cadiz area the soles taken from the salt pans before the sea water dries are called 'de estero'; hence 'lenguado de estero', which is likely to appear on a restaurant menu, since these soles are fatter and especially tasty, probably because of the high temperature and high salt content of the water in the salt pans.

Incidentally, the harvesting of the fish from the salt pans is called 'despesque' and a party is held on the spot, the fish (often alive) being grilled there and then on a fire made with glasswort, the plant that covers the marshy land around. The fish are eaten with the fingers: 'simply delicious', says one who has taken part in this festivity.

Villoch, in his admirable new book on species of the fish auctions in Galicia, thinks it worthwhile to provide anyone who has ordered sole in a restaurant with a tip for distinguishing this species, the true and best sole, from the not-quite-so-good acedía, Galician name for *Solea lascaris* (next page). Look at the 'white side' of the fish. If the nostril bulges up like a wart, it is the latter; if not, the former. The 'wart' does not disappear as a result of the fish being cooked.

Solea senegalensis
LENGUADO SENEGALÉS   SENEGAL SOLE

Gal: /
Bas: /
Cat: /
Por: linguado branco
Fre: /
Ger: /

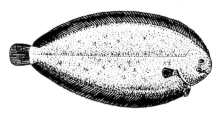

The second largest sole of the region (max <> 60, mkt <> 30–45), is much less common than *S vulgaris* (preceding page). It has a range from the Bay of Biscay down to Senegal and appears only rarely in the West Mediterranean.

Solea lascaris
SORTIJA, LENGUADO   SAND SOLE
DE ARENA

Gal: acedía, lenguado bravo
Bas: hare lengoradu
Cat: llenguado
Por: linguado da areia,
    cascarro, macaca
Fre: sole pôle
Ger: /

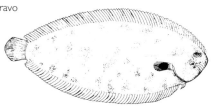

Max <> 40, mkt <> around 25. The back is yellowish brown with spots which may be more or less distinct. The skin is very rough to the touch.

Generally, this sole is not greatly esteemed, although in some markets it commands a good price.

Solea kleini
SUELA   KLEIN'S SOLE

Gal: /   Por: linguado revesso
Bas: /   Fre: sole tachetée
Cat: /   Ger: /

Similar to the preceding species in size and shape; distinguished by a dark spot on the pectoral fin, a feature also found in the similar but smaller species *S impar* (sometimes called Adriatic sole).

Microchirus variegatus

GOLLETA   THICKBACK SOLE

Gal: lirpia raiada
Bas: lengoradu pinto
Cat: pelut, soldat
Por: azevia, tapa
Fre: sole perdrix
Ger: Bastardzunge

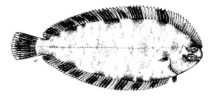

Max <> 20 (occasionally more), mkt <> 12–15. Of good quality; hence the French name, likening it to a partridge.

Microchirus ocellatus

TAMBOR REAL   FOUR-EYED SOLE

Gal: /
Bas: /
Cat: soldat
Por: azevia, linguado
Fre: sole ocellée
Ger: /

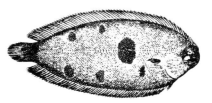

Max <> 20, mkt <> around 15. The large dark spot and the four 'eyes' constitute distinctive markings. The species occurs throughout the Mediterranean, but in the East Atlantic it keeps to the south of the Strait of Gibraltar.

Monochirus hispidus

SOLDADO   WHISKERED SOLE

Gal: /
Bas: /
Cat: lenguado de fonera,
    peluda d'alga
Por: cascarra
Fre: sole velue
Ger: /

Another small species; max <> 20, mkt <> 10–15. This sole has no pectoral fin on the blind side. Its common names mostly indicate its 'shaggy' appearance.

Family BALISTIDAE
Balistes carolinensis

PEZ BALLESTA   TRIGGER FISH

Gal: pez ballesta
Bas: baleztarrain
Cat: bot
Por: cangulo
Fre: baliste
Ger: Drückerfisch

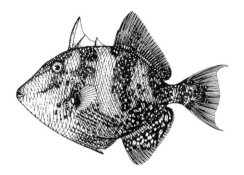

Max <> 48, mkt <> 15–35. 'Trigger' refers to the interlocking effect of the three stiff spines at the front of the dorsal fin. The skin of this fish is thick and leathery; but the flesh is good. Found in the Mediterranean and both sides of the Atlantic, but usually in small numbers and only in places which suit it. Rare in Galician waters, although reputedly found around Cies Island offshore from Vigo.

Family LOPHIIDAE
Lophius piscatorius

RAPE   ANGLER-FISH

Gal: rape, (peixe) sapo, xuliana   *Por:* tamboril
Bas: zapo zuri   *Fre:* baudroie
Cat: rap, granota de mar   *Ger:* Seeteufel

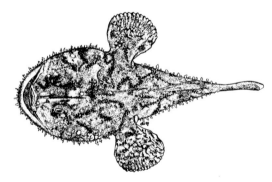

Max <> 150 mkt <> 40–90. However, in some markets and many shops only the rear end of this fish is sold, the huge head being discarded (though it makes a fine soup).

The very similar but smaller *L budegassa* (max <> 80) may be distinguished by its having a dark membrane covering the edible part, whereas *L piscatorius* has a white membrane.

L budegassa is preferred in Galicia, where it has the name verdadero rape (true angler-fish). The Basque name is zapo beltz.

In Madrid and generally in northern Spain the name rabada is used for the less good species.

The angler-fish, often under the name 'monk' or 'monkfish', has become popular in Britain since the 1960s; and the corresponding American species (*L americanus*: common name goosefish) has since the 1970s been considered edible in some parts of the USA. The flesh is free of small bones and has a very firm consistency – can, indeed, be passed off as lobster (for which it makes an acceptable substitute in the Portuguese Açorda de Marisco, a fishy bread soup). Colas de Pixin al Gril or a la Plancha will be grilled tail ends.

Angler-fish is also considered to be a fine ingredient for a Caldeirada (see page 11). Another well-known dish of the region of Asturias and Santander is Rape a la Sidra, angler-fish cooked in cider.

Family PETROMYZONIDAE
Petromyzon marinus

LAMPREA DE MAR   SEA LAMPREY

Gal: lamprea, chupona   *Por:* lampreia do mar
Bas: itsas lanproi   *Fre:* lamproie marine
Cat: llampresa de mar   *Ger:* Meerneunauge

Max <> 120, mkt <> 50–80. The sea lamprey may be found in the lower reaches and tributaries of half a dozen major rivers: the Ebro; the Guadalquivir; the Guadiana; the Tagus; the Minho; and the Ulla.

These fish are exceptionally primitive, adapted to living as parasites on larger fish or marine mammals, whose blood they suck.

They are greatly appreciated as food in Galicia and the north of Portugal. Usually eaten in an empanada (pie) or cooked in their own blood (Lamprea a la Cazuela) and served on a bed of white rice. In the north of Portugal this dish is known as Lampreia à Moda do Minho.

SHARKS

We come now to what are called the 'non-bony' fish. One might suppose the term to indicate that they are free of those irritating little bones which bother people when they eat members of the herring family, for example. In fact, they are free of these annoyances. But what is meant is that their skeletons are not of real bone at all, but merely cartilaginous. The 'non-bony' fish include sharks and rays.

For those who are not fishermen, sharks are perceived more as sources of danger than as food. However, few are dangerous to human beings, whereas there are many species which are edible, or even very good to eat. This category includes the relatively small dogfish.

Given their size, and the repellent aspect of many of them, sharks are usually skinned and cut up before sale.

Family SPHYRNIDAE
Sphyrna zygaena

PEZ MARTILLO   HAMMERHEAD

Gal: peixe martelo   *Por:* martelo
Bas: mailuarrain   *Fre:* requin marteau
Cat: llunada   *Ger:* Hammerhai

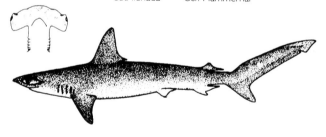

Max <> 400, normal mature <> 220 (male) or 300 (female). The extraordinary shape of the head makes this shark immediately recognizable.

In Galicia, this is considered to be the best shark for eating. The liver produces an oil rich in vitamins.

I once cooked a whole hammerhead shark by poaching it in a court-bouillon. This feat was only possible because it was a baby, not more than 55 cm long; but it worked well.

Family LAMNIDAE

Lamna nasus

CAILÓN   PORBEAGLE SHARK

Gal: marraxo
Bas: marratzo muturmotz
Cat: marraix

Por: marracho
Fre: taupe
Ger: Heringshai

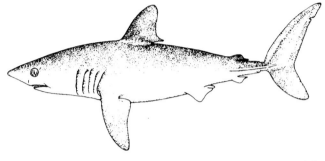

Max <> around 300, common <> 100–250. The flesh of the porbeagle is esteemed in Galicia, and perhaps even more so in Germany, where much of the European catch finishes up (although some is also exported to Asian countries).

Isurus oxyrinchus

MARRAJO   SHORTFIN MAKO

Gal: marraxo azul
Bas: marrazo muturluze
Cat: solraig

Por: marracho
Fre: requin-taupe bleu
Ger: /

Max <> 400. Sold in Galicia in the summer months, and in the south of Spain too. Good white flesh, suitable for any standard methods of preparation, and sometimes passed off as swordfish.

However, the mako is rated below the porbeagle. Lower still down the scale comes *Prionace glauca* (Spanish **tintorera**, Galician quenlla, Portuguese guelha), sometimes taken along with swordfish.

Family ALOPIIDAE
Alopias vulpinus

PEZ ZORRO   THRESHER SHARK

Gal: raposo do mar, camarín
Bas: itsas azeri
Cat: guineu

Por: zorro, raposo
Fre: renard de mer
Ger: Fuchshai

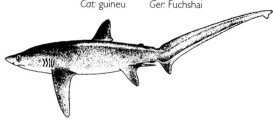

Max <> 400 (male) or 600 (female), ie a huge creature. But much of the length is taken up by the long 'tail', which the fishermen usually cut off and discard as soon as they have taken a fish. The rest of the fish, and of the related *A superciliosus* is sometimes sold in Galicia. The drawing, as it happens, is of the latter species.

Family SCYLIORHINIDAE
Scyliorhinus stellaris

ALITÁN   NURSE-HOUND

Gal: roxa, patarroxa
Bas: momar
Cat: gatvaire

Por: gata
Fre: grande roussette
Ger: groogefleckter Katzenhai

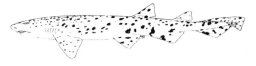

Max <> 150 (in the Mediterranean), mkt <> 40–55.

This and similar small sharks of the category often referred to in English as dogfish (and often with names in other languages meaning the same) provide good eating; the flesh would not do for really fancy dishes, but serves well for everyday fare.

Scyliorhinus canicula

PINTARROJA

LESSER-SPOTTED DOGFISH

Gal: melgacho, can do mar
Bas: katuarrain
Cat: gat, gato

Por: pintaroxa
Fre: petite roussette
Ger: kleingefleckter Katzenhai

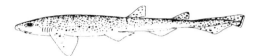

Max <> 80 (in the Mediterranean), mkt <> 20–50.
 Best eaten in a casserole (guisado) or caldeirada.

Galeus melastomus

BOCANEGRA

BLACKMOUTHED DOGFISH

Gal: sapata
Bas: pinpirin, kolaio
Cat: moisina

Por: letão
Fre: chien espagnol
Ger: Fleckhai

Max <> just over 50 in the Mediterranean, up to 100 elsewhere, mkt <> 20–50. The inside of the mouth is entirely
black, which accounts for many of the names.
 One of the smaller dogfish, quite good as dogfish go.

ROSADA

This name is often applied in Spain to fillets of any of
several small sharks or dogfish. These fillets are popular
fare and readily available.

Mustelus mustelus

MUSOLA   SMOOTH-HOUND

Gal: cazón
Bas: toil liso
Cat: mussola

Por: cação pieque
Fre: emissole lisse
Ger: Glatthai

Max <> 160, mkt <> 60–120. Back and sides are plain grey.

These sharks make tolerably good eating, but are not in great demand. Best cooked as fillets with plenty of added flavour.

Mustelus asterias

MUSOLA CORONADA   STELLATE SMOOTH-HOUND

Gal: cazón blanco
Bas: toil pikart
Cat: /

Por: caneja, cação
Fre: emissole tachetée
Ger: Glatthai

Max <> 140, mkt <> 50–100. The back bears lots of tiny white spots (hence the name *asterias*, meaning starry), but otherwise this shark looks just like the one above, so no drawing is needed. Insofar as any distinction is made between the two species, this one is generally thought to be inferior.

Galeorhinus galeus

CAZÓN   TOPE SHARK

Gal: cazón
Bas: gelba
Cat: caço

Por: perna de moça
Fre: milandre
Ger: Hundshai

A larger member of the family; max <> nearly 200, common <> 90–150. Whereas the smooth-hounds have, as one would expect, smooth skins, the tope has skin like sandpaper.

The tope provides sport for sea anglers throughout its extensive range, from Norway to Morocco and the East Mediterranean (also on the coasts of California, South America, South Africa, Australia, etc).

The tope is one of the best sharks for eating, with a liver exceptionally rich in vitamin A and fins which are good for sharkfin soup. In the south of Spain the dish Cazón en Amarillo is well known; this is tope stewed with onion and potatoes and peas, with saffron to give it a golden-yellow colour.

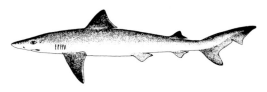

Family SQUALIDAE
Squalus acanthias

MIELGA   SPUR DOG

Gal: melga, melja, boto
Bas: mielga pikart
Cat: agullat, ferró

Por: melga
Fre: aiguillat tacheté
Ger: Dornhai

Max <> in the Mediterranean 140 (more elsewhere); mkt <> 65–100. The grey sides bear small white spots. The dorsal fins each begin with one spiny ray.

In the closely related species *S blainvillei* (= *S fernandinus*) these spiny rays are longer and more prominent, the white spots are lacking, and the nose is a little longer. It is illustrated below.

These are two species with a world-wide distribution – indeed some authorities think that *S acanthias* may be the most abundant of all sharks. Neither species is in much demand in the Spanish and Portuguese markets, although both may appear. There seems to be some trade in smoked fillets, but I have not tried these myself.

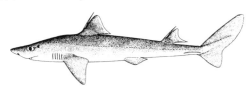

Family SQUATINIDAE
Squatina squatina
ANGELOTE, PEZ ANGEL ANGEL SHARK

Gal: peixe anxel   *Por:* pexe anjo
Bas: aingeru goardako   *Fre:* ange de mer
Cat: escat   *Ger:* Meerengel

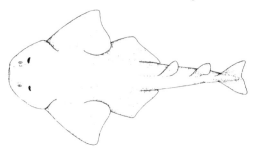

Max <> 180 or more, mkt <> 40–150. Officially a shark, but tending in shape so far towards the rays and skates that it is really an 'in between' creature.

Living in Tunisia, I and my family greatly enjoyed eating the angel shark; but it is not widely popular. Our favourite recipe involved baking portions of it with garlic, tomato and olives.

Family RHINOBATIDAE
Rhinobatos rhinobatos
GUITARRA GUITARFISH

Gal: peixe guitarra   *Por:* viola
Bas: kitarrarrain   *Fre:* poisson guitare
Cat: /   *Ger:* Geigenroche

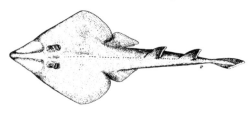

Max <> 100, mkt <> around 75. Another species of an intermediate sort, between sharks and rays.

Not held in high esteem, but sometimes marketed.

RAYS AND SKATES

The rays resemble the sharks in two respects; they are fish without true bones, and they are numerous. The species shown on this page is the best for eating, and so regarded throughout Europe. The others, the subject of short entries on the following three pages, are less good but still worth catching, marketing and cooking.

Spain is one of the countries where considerable knowledge of and discrimination between rays is exhibited, although, with a few exceptions, the same common names are applied to all (eg raya in Spain, raia in Galician, arraia in Basque).

Family RAJIDAE
Raja clavata

RAYA DE CLAVOS, RAYA COMMUN   THORNBACK RAY

Gal: raia raspiñeira
Bas: (arraia) gastaka
Cat: clavell
Por: raia pregada
Fre: raie bouclée
Ger: Nagelrochen

Max <> 100, mkt <> 30–80. The back, which is usually mottled grey or light brown in colour, bears what are at first coarse prickles and then, in fully adult fish, spines with swollen and bony bases (called 'bucklers').

The thornback has a range which extends far north in the Atlantic besides taking in the whole of the Mediterranean and the Black Sea. It makes limited migrations, travelling in unisexual shoals; so that fishermen are likely to catch either a lot of males or a lot of females, but not a mixture of the two.

Rays have an ammoniac smell which puts some people off eating them. However, it should not do so. The truth is that non-bony fish such as rays and sharks use a chemical substance, urea, to control their osmotic balance (ie ensure that water does not constantly leach out of them into the sea or vice versa). On death, the urea starts to break up, producing ammonia and the ammoniac smell. But this is good, since one wants the urea to go away; and in any event cooking will get rid of all traces of ammonia.

Raja alba

RAYA ALBA, RAYA BRAMANTE   WHITE SKATE

Gal:
Bas: arraia marrazuri
Cat:
Por: raia tairoga
Fre: raie blanche
Ger: Bandrochen

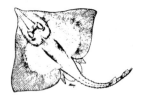

Raja asterias

RAYA ESTRELLADA   STARRY RAY

Gal:
Bas: /
Cat: grisol, llisol
Por: raia pintada
Fre: raie étoilée
Ger: Sternrochen

Raja batis

NORIEGA   SKATE

Gal: ferreiro
Bas: arraia azpilun
Cat: /
Por: raia oirega
Fre: pocheteau gris
Ger: Glattrochen

Raja brachyura

RAYA BOCA DE ROSA   BLONDE RAY

Gal: raia pintada
Bas: arraia isatslabur
Cat: /
Por: raia pontuada
Fre: raie lisse
Ger: /

Raja fullonica

RAYA CARDADORA   SHAGREEN RAY

Gal: bicudo
Bas: txarrantxa-arraia
Cat: /
Por: raia pregada
Fre: raie chardon
Ger: Chagrinrochen

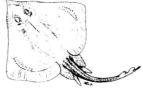

Max <> 110, mkt <> 35–70. More common in the Atlantic.

Raja miraletus

RAYA DE ESPEJOS   BROWN RAY

Gal: /
Bas: /
Cat: rajada de taques
Por: raia de quatro olhos
Fre: raie miroir
Ger: Spiegelrochen

Max <> 60, mkt <> 20–50. More common in the Mediterranean.

Raja montagui

RAYA PINTADA   SPOTTED RAY

Gal: /
Bas: arraia pikart
Cat: /
Por: raia manchada
Fre: raie douce
Ger: gefleckter Rochen

Max <> 80, mkt <> 40–60.

Raja naevus

RAYA SANTIAGUESA   CUCKOO RAY

Gal: raia santiaguesa
Bas: /
Cat: menjamoisines
Por: raia de dois olhos
Fre: raie fleurie
Ger: Kuckucksrochen

Max <> 70, mkt <> 30–50.

Raja oxyrinchus

PICON LONGNOSED SKATE

Gal: raia bicuda
Bas: moko-arraia
Cat: caputxó, càvec
Por: raia bicuda
Fre: pocheteau noir
Ger: /

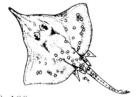

Max <> 150, mkt <> 50–100.

Raja radula

RAYA ASPERA ROUGH RAY

Gal: /
Bas: /
Cat: /
Por: /
Fre: raie râpe
Ger: /

Max <> 70, mkt <> 20–50.

Raja undulata

RAYA MOSAICA UNDULATE RAY

Gal: gramante (doubtful name)
Bas: arraia uhindu
Cat: /
Por: raia curva
Fre: raie brunette
Ger: /

Max <> 100, mkt <> 40–60. This species seems to be marketed more in Morocco than elsewhere.

STURGEON

In a class by itself. Following the 'bony' and 'non-bony' fish, we come to a fish whose skeleton is part bony and part not (the backbone is cartilaginous, but the bony scutes on the body and the bony plates on the armoured head are of true bone), a creature which has survived a hundred million years or more, which used to be so plentiful in western Europe that in Galicia, for example, its flesh was used as fertilizer and its eggs (precious caviar!) fed to pigs. And yet, after a history of abundance extending over many centuries, the sturgeon seems to be doomed, at least in Europe, to near extinction, doomed by the activities of 20th-century man.

Sturgeon were well known in the Guadalquivir in former times, and used to be fished when they came in to spawn; but it seems that the last catch in that river, of a female, was in the mid 1980s. Likewise, it was still possible in the early 1980s to find juvenile sturgeon in the Guadiana and Duero; but not any more.

Family ACIPENSERIDAE

Acipenser sturio

ESTURIÓN   STURGEON

Gal: sollo rei   *Por:* esturjão real
Bas: gaizkata, zoilu   *Fre:* esturgeon
Cat: esturió   *Ger:* Stör

Max <> 350, mkt <> 100–150 (male) or 130–215 (female). This species has the typical sturgeon snout, equipped with barbels underneath, with which to forage for food on the sea or river bottom. (Some sturgeon belong to fresh waters only, while others live at sea but migrate into estuaries and rivers; this species belongs to the latter group.)

The meat of the sturgeon has often been compared to veal, and the comparison has some validity; it can serve as a guide to various ways of cooking sturgeon: frying thin slices, grilling thicker ones, cooking 'joints' in the same way as large pieces of veal, etc.

CRUSTACEANS

The animal phylum Arthropoda includes creatures of both land (spiders, scorpions, and numerous insects) and sea (shrimp, prawns, lobsters and crabs). A high proportion of marine crustaceans, at least of those which attain a reasonable size, are edible; and some of them are exceptionally good.

It is a characteristic of crustaceans that they shed their hard carapaces from time to time, to permit growth. In general, it is good to choose specimens whose carapaces are encrusted and therefore old, since a crustacean in a brand-new carapace will be smaller than you expect, not yet having grown fully to fit it. Another characteristic is that crustaceans change colour markedly when cooked; eg a dark blue lobster will turn red. However, some prawns are already pink or red when alive.

The most unusual crustacean catalogued here, the percebe on page 142, happens also to be one of the great seafood specialities of both Spain and Portugal. Timorous visitors, not knowing how to eat them and fearing to make an exhibition of themselves, are apt to miss a remarkable experience; there is nothing else, in my view, which quite matches eating percebes for a true 'taste of the sea'.

Family CRANGONIDAE
Crangon crangon
QUISQUILLA (GRIS/D'ARENA)   BROWN SHRIMP

Gal: camarón, esquila
Bas: izkira zuri,
     izkira grisa
Cat: gamba d'esquer
Por: camarão negro/mouro
Fre: crevette grise
Ger: sand Garnele

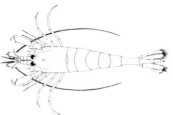

Max <> 6, mkt <> 4 or 5. A semi-transparent grey creature with dark spots.

These small shrimp have many uses, for example in combination seafood platters, in seafood dishes with rice, in soups and in sauces. In Portugal, look out for the delicious Rissois de Camarão, sold at every pâtisserie in the country and an almost obligatory savoury at parties or served as snacks or light meals. (They are deep-fried 'rissoles', the dough casing filled with cooked and shelled shrimps in a white sauce with lemon juice, nutmeg etc.)

Palaemon serratus (= Leander serratus)

CAMARÓN (DE ROCA), COMMON PRAWN
QUISQUILLA

Gal: camarón   *Por:* camarão do rio
Bas: izkira gorri   *Fre:* crevette rose
Cat: gamba, gambeta   *Ger:* Sägegarnele

Max <> 11, mkt <> about 7. See the drawing below right.

A typical fishery for the camarón is conducted near the mouth of the Guadalquivir, using 'spoon' nets from anchored boats. At Trebujena, in the nearby sherry-producing area, people make Tortillitas de Camarones; these are not small omelettes, as the name would suggest, but thin biscuit-like confections, made by crisply frying the shrimps, shell and all, in batter.

Common names in Spain for this species and for *Crangon crangon* (on the preceding page) are apt to overlap. The same applies to, for example, *Pasiphaea sivada*, the 'white glass shrimp' of deep waters (usually camarón blanco in Spanish), and to at least half a dozen other shrimp or small prawns which may come to market from more distant fishing grounds or be caught locally in Iberian waters.

In the latter category, and in the family Pandalidae, it is worth mentioning *Plesionika edwardsi*, the soldier shrimp or camarón soldado (Basque, izkiratzar): max <> 16, mkt <> around 10, reddish in colour. See the drawing below left. This species is found also in West Atlantic waters.

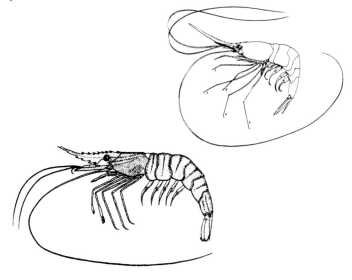

Aristeus antennatus

CARABINERO   PRAWN

Gal: /	*Por:* gamba rosada
Bas: /	*Fre:* crevette rouge/rose
Cat: gamba rosada	*Ger:* /

Max <> 22, mkt <> around 10–18. Among the best large prawns of the Mediterranean. It is of a rosy colour; and in Cadiz is called chorizo (after the Spanish sausage), because of the red juices which it exudes; see below for the similar Galician and Catalan names for the next species.

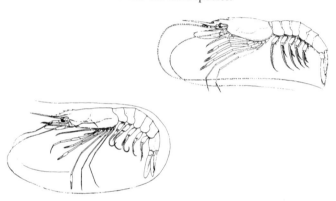

The species *Aristeomorpha foliacea*, shown in the lower drawing, is similar but larger, and has a blood-red body with a violet headpiece. It is **langostino moruno** in Spanish (but neither it nor *Penaeus kerathurus*, page 131, should be confused with what the French call langoustine, page 133). It can also be **gamba roja** in Spanish; and is chourizo in Galician, ganba gorri in Basque, gamba vermelha or xoriço in Catalan.

A similar species, *Plesiopenaeus edwardsianus*, belongs to the Atlantic and is rare in the West Mediterranean; it is carabinero in both Spain and Portugal, and gambota in the Balearics.

The prawns on this page are very good, and some would say that those on the next page, especially *Penaeus kerathurus*, are even better. So this is a suitable place to say something about prawn cookery.

Popular hot prawn dishes in Spain include Gambas a la Plancha (grilled), Gambas al Ajillo (in an earthenware casserole with garlic, hot chilli pepper and olive oil) and Gambas al Pil-pil (see page 29). The Portuguese too like the 'al ajillo' dish, and enjoy Gambas Picantes (with hot little chilli peppers and garlic); they also enjoy having the prawns poached in beer or white wine to be served as appetizers.

Cold cooked prawns abound in Spanish tapas bars, often partnered by Allioli (garlic mayonnaise), or other sauces.

Family PENAEIDAE
Penaeus kerathurus

LANGOSTINO   PRAWN

Gal: langostino   *Por:* gamba amarela
Bas: otarrainska   *Fre:* caramote
Cat: llagostí   *Ger:* Caramote

Another large prawn; max <> 22 (females), mkt <> around 16. It is brown with reddish tints. See the upper drawing.

The Spanish name is very close to the well-known French name langoustine, which applies, however, to something quite different, the Norway lobster (see page 133).

The langostino is exceptionally good, perhaps especially in the region of Cadiz, where the 'langostino de Sanlucar' has a great and well-deserved reputation.

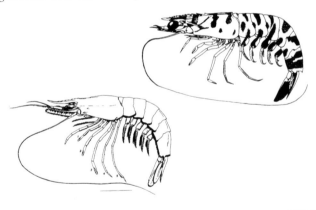

Parapenaeus longirostris

GAMBA   PRAWN

Gal: gamba, jamba   *Por:* gamba
Bas: ganba zuri   *Fre:* crevette rose du large
Cat: gamba (blanca)   *Ger:* Garnele

Max <> 19 (females), mkt <> 8–16. Red/orange in colour, with the beak more definitely red and the underside of the body seeming to be violet. See lower drawing.

A valuable prawn, regularly seen in the markets.

Homarus gammarus

BOGAVANTE (EUROPEAN) LOBSTER

Gal: lumbrigante, bugre
Bas: abakando
Cat: llòmantol

Por: lavagante
Fre: homard
Ger: Hummer

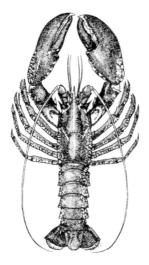

This and its very close relation, the American lobster, *H americanus*, may grow to a great size (a specimen more than a metre in length and weighing 20 kg was recorded on the American side of the Atlantic) but giants of that order of magnitude are unknown nowadays and the usual mkt <> is 25–50.

It is unnecessary to praise the merits of the lobster or to enumerate famous ways of preparing it. However, it may be worth pointing out that the high price it commands reflects the effort involved in catching it, as well as its intrinsic good qualities; and that the humbler and more easily caught crab may (in my view) be equally delicious.

An unusual lobster dish in the Catalan region is Bogavante con Salsa de Chocolate, which can also be prepared using spiny lobster (and rabbit).

Nephrops norvegicus

CIGALA,★ MAGANTO   NORWAY LOBSTER, DUBLIN BAY PRAWN

Gal: cigala, langostino,
  patas largas
Bas: zigala
Cat: escamarlà
Por: lagostim
Fre: langoustine
Ger: Kaisergranat

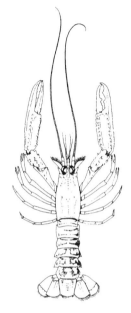

The Norway lobster or Dublin Bay prawn, better known in many places by the plural Italian name, 'scampi', is considerably smaller than the true lobster: max <> 24, mkt <> around 10–20. It has an extensive range, from Norway (obviously) down to certain parts of the Mediterranean. It does not congregate in Dublin Bay, as one might suppose, but got that name because catches of it were unloaded there to be hawked round the streets of Dublin.

Although small for a lobster, it can just as well be regarded as large in comparison to most prawns; and there is certainly enough meat on it to make it well worth eating. It may be prepared in any of the ways suitable for large prawns; or cut in half lengthways and grilled (Cigalas a la Plancha).

★ Confusing, because of the French name cigale which is used of the flat lobster (page 135). In Spain the Norway lobster is also known as langostina. The latter name, like the Galician langostino, conveniently echoes the familiar French name langoustine, but can cause confusion since it is applied in Spain to certain prawns (see page 131).

Palinurus elephas (= P vulgaris)

LANGOSTA   SPINY LOBSTER

Gal: langosta   *Por:* lagosta
Bas: otarrain   *Fre:* langouste
Cat: llagosta   *Ger:* Langoste

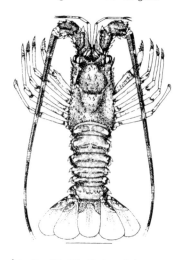

Max <> 50, mkt <> 25-35. Spiny lobsters
belong to warmer waters than their cousin the Atlantic lobster
(page 132) and lack the large claws which it possesses. The
species shown above, of a generally brownish/red/purple coloration, is the most common in Spanish and Portuguese
waters, but there are two others: the larger (max <> 75) *P
mauritanicus*, mainly fished from the North-West African coast;
and *Panulirus* (not a misprint, a different genus) *regius*. The former of these two is generally rosy or reddish in colour, and is
langosta mora in Spain, langouste rose in France. The latter is
greenish, so is called langosta verde (or langosta real) in Spain.

Except that they do not provide claw meat, these crustaceans
can be treated like the Atlantic lobster. Some prefer them, and
some prefer the Atlantic lobster; but everyone agrees that they
are delicious. In Portugal they count as the supreme seafood
treat, and are usually plain boiled (poached) and served with
mayonnaise.

Family SCYLLARIDAE
Scyllarides latus

CIGARRA   FLAT LOBSTER

Gal: cigarra de mar   *Por:* lagosta da pedra
Bas: santio handi   *Fre:* (grande) cigale
Cat: cigala (gran), sapa,   *Ger:* (grosser) Bärenkrebs
esclop

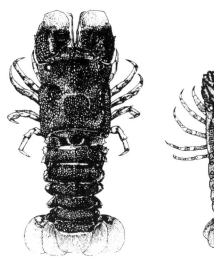
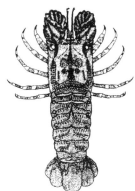

Mkt <> 15–35. A Mediterranean species, shown above left. Although this crustacean's English names all incorporate 'lobster' (thus flat lobster, slipper lobster, rock lobster, etc), it is not of the same family as true lobsters. Nor does it make such good eating. However, the 'tail' (correctly, the abdomen) of large specimens provides a substantial amount of lobster-like meat. Small specimens are best used in fish soups.

The same applies to a small relation, *S arctus*, usually about 10–12 cm long and more common in the Atlantic (illustrated above right). In some languages this creature has names indicating its relatively small size (eg the French petite cigale de mer), but in Galician its various names include the unusual caballero de Santiago, which finds an echo in the Castilian name santiaguiño; these are references to the 'cross of Santiago' on the carapace. The Portuguese name is bruxa.

Both species have a general coloration of reddish brown, the former tending more towards grey.

Family CANCRIDAE

Cancer pagurus

BUEY (EDIBLE/COMMON) CRAB

Gal: boi (de Francia)
Bas: buia, petaca
Cat: buey

Por: sapateira
Fre: tourteau
Ger: Taschenkrebs

A large crab whose 'shell' (carapace) is likely to measure 10–20 cm across in the markets. This is an Atlantic species, not found in the Mediterranean.

Probably the best crab of all, at least in Europe. Both the brown (body) and white (claw) meat are delicious. Plain 'dressed crab' is the most popular way of presenting it.

There is a deep-water relation, *Cancer bellianus*, which may be called buey (or boi) de altura. It is fished at a depth of 500 metres or so, often from waters to the south of Ireland.

American readers will be interested to know that their famous blue crab, *Callinectes sapidus*, has migrated to the Mediterranean and established itself in various parts thereof. It has already found its way, as **cangrejo azul**, into the official wall-chart of crabs of the Spanish coasts; and it seems likely that during the 1990s it will be visible in Spanish markets, perhaps first in the Balearics. It is mentioned on this page because it matches in size and excellence the edible crab shown above; but it belongs to the family Portunidae, at which we arrive on the next page. The small drawing of it below shows clearly the 'swimming legs' which are a characteristic of that family.

Carcinus aestuarii and C maenas

CANGREJO COMUN (OR DE MAR)

SHORE CRAB

Gal: cangrexo
Bas: karramarro berde
Cat: cranc verd

Por: caranguejo
Fre: crabe vert
Ger: Strandkrabbe

Max <> 7, mkt <> 4-5 across the 'shell', which is greenish.

Of these two very similar species, it is the second which is shown in the drawing; it is an Atlantic crab, which penetrates only a short way into the Mediterranean. *C aestuarii*, on the other hand, is more at home in the Mediterranean and indeed used to be classified as *C mediterraneus*.

Either species is suited for use in fish soups.

NOTE The Galician name cangrexo may also appear with the adjective 'real'. Although the crab to which this name refers, *Geryon affinis*, is not at all common in the markets, even in Galicia, it merits a brief note, since the Galician fishery authorities have decided recently (1990) to promote the capture and marketing of crabs of this species. They are deep-water crabs, of the family Geryonidae, and constitute for Spain a 'new' species which has the advantage of existing in Spanish waters.

There was no fishery for them in the past because of the difficulty of fishing at great depths (500 metres or more), but these difficulties seem to have been overcome.

Males, which are considerably larger than females, may weigh as much as 2.5 kg. Normal weights are 1 kg for a male and 400 g for a female.

Necora puber (= Macropipus/Liocarcinus/Portunus puber)

NÉCORA   SWIMMING CRAB

Gal: nécora
Bas: txamar, nekora
Cat: nécora

Por: pilado, navalheira
Fre: étrille
Ger: Schwimmkrabbe

Another small crab, max <> 8, mkt <> 5–6 across the carapace. This one is regarded as superior to the preceding species, but it too, because of its small size, is normally consigned to the soup pot.

Other small swimming crabs in Iberian waters include, for example:
Liocarcinus corrugatus (Castilian, **cambaro mazorgano**; Galician, nécora francesa or conguito; Catalan, franquet vermell), used in soups (shown below left);
Macropipus depurator (Galician, patulate), edible and eaten but of no commercial interest (shown below right); and
Portumnus latipes, an even smaller species which is not infrequently used in the preparation of a paella (not illustrated).

Eriphia verrucosa (= *E spinifrons*)

CANGREJO MORUNO   FURRY CRAB

Gal: rabuda
Bas: ezkarra
Cat: cranc pelut
Por: caranguejo da pedra
Fre: ériphie
Ger: /

A smallish (max <> 10, mkt <> 7) and somewhat furry creature which has powerful pincers. It is prized as food in the south of France and in the Balearics and parts of the Mediterranean coast of Spain (especially as an ingredient for paella).

Calappa granulata

CANGREJO REAL   SHAMEFACED CRAB

Gal: boi bravo
Bas: karramarro lotsati
Cat: franquet dormidor, pessic
Por: aurora
Fre: crabe honteux/granuleux
Ger: /

Max <> 10, mkt <> about 7 across the carapace. Another minor crab, suitable as an ingredient in soups.

The same applies to yet another, which is shown below. This is *Pachygrapsus marmoratus* (Spanish, **cangrejo de roca**; French, crabe marbré; Galician, queimacasas; Basque, karramarro beltz; Catalan, cranc (or franquet) de roca; Portuguese corta camisas). Max <> 10, mkt <> 5. The carapace is brown with grey-green marbling.

Maja squinado

CENTOLLA SPIDER CRAB

Gal: centola, pateiro *Por:* santola
Bas: txangurro *Fre:* araignée
Cat: cabra *Ger:* (grosse) Seespine

Max <> 25 x 18, mkt <> about 15 x 12, for the carapace, which is reddish in colour.

A large and beautiful crab, with names which indicate the resemblance which it bears to a spider. It is an artist in camouflage, and will even 'plant' living organisms on its carapace to help it escape the attention of predators.

The meat is good. It is commonly prepared with added flavours such as garlic, and presented stuffed in the shell. In the Basque country this is Txangurro Relleno. Txangurro al Horno is another name for this sort of dish.

There is such a demand for the spider crab in Portugal and Spain that local supplies have become insufficient and the crabs are being imported from as far away as Cornwall in England; this, anyway, applies to Portugal. In the north of Spain, what seems to be a variety of *M squinado*, coming from France and known locally by names such as centola francesa, may be met in the markets. Its carapace is thicker, less rough and less likely to be 'planted' with other organisms. It is considered to be inferior in quality, but I have not myself had an opportunity to make a comparison.

A somewhat similar crab from the southern hemisphere, *Lithodes antarcticus* (**centolla chilena** in Spanish) is being marketed in Spain as a substitute for the true native centolla.

Family OCYPODIDAE

Uca tangeri

BARRILETE, BOCA (of the claw)   AFRICAN FIDDLER CRAB

Gal: /
Bas: /
Cat: /
Por: cava-terra
Fre: /
Ger: Winkerkrabbe

A strange crab which can give the impression of being a violinist or fiddler by the manner in which it 'saws' its big claw up and down, standing on the shore (or in solemn rows on the bank of a river, like an orchestra, as I saw them in Trinidad).

In the Cadiz region the most famous of these crabs live in holes on the muddy banks of the inlets which carry water to the Cadiz salt pans around Sanfernando, near Cadiz, which is still called 'the island'. So they are called 'bocas de la isla'. They are not sold whole. The fishermen remove from the male the one large claw and then return the live crab to the water, so that it can grow another large claw for the following season. The claws have a delicious flavour: truly unique, say connoisseurs in Cadiz.

Family SQUILLIDAE

Squilla mantis

GALERA   MANTIS SHRIMP

Gal: araña
Bas: /
Cat: galera
Por: zagaia
Fre: squille
Ger: Heuschreckenkrebs

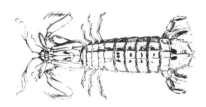

Max <> 20, mkt <> around 12–18. An oddity, not a real shrimp, nor a crab, but a creature belonging to a different order, Stomatopoda. As this name indicates, its front 'legs' are extensions of its mouth; and it is the marine counterpart of the praying mantis.

Can be used in fish soups. Better known in Italy than in Spain.

Family POLLICIPIDAE
Mitella pollicipes (=Pollicipes cornucopia)
PERCEBE   GOOSE-NECKED BARNACLE

Gal: percebe
Bas: lanperna
Cat: perçebe, peu de cabrit
Por: perceve
Fre: pouce-pied
Ger: Seepocke

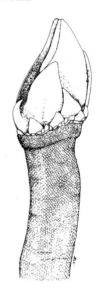

Impossible to give a 'market length' for this strange creature, since it turns up in smaller or larger pieces, depending on how many of them have been broken off the rocks on which they live in groups. However, for what it is worth, the notice displayed at the fish market in Santiago de Compostela, giving minimum legal lengths for all kinds of seafood, says that a percebe must be at least 4 cm long.

It is a crustacean, although not looking remotely like a prawn or crab. It consists of what might be called a tube, as thick as a finger, covered by a dark and scaly skin. At the end is a sort of 'hoof', white bony pads from between which the creature's feet emerge.

Although the most magnificent percebe belongs to Chile, where it is greatly prized, these strange creatures are generally regarded as a speciality of Spain and Portugal, where the taste for them is well developed and on whose coasts there are plenty of suitable rocks to provide a habitat.

To eat, pinch the outer skin near the hoofs and prise it off with your fingernails, revealing a stalk-like protuberance which you bite off whole. Percebes can be eaten raw, but those offered in bars and restaurants have usually been cooked, briefly, and are the better for this.

SINGLE SHELLS

The marine creatures which live in single shells are numerous, and many are edible, but only a few of them are sufficiently good to appear in the markets or on menus.

Our list starts with the relatively large ormer or abalone, familiar to North Americans because of the importance of the related species off the coast of California and the Pacific North-West generally.

Family HALIOTIDAE
Haliotis tuberculata

OREJA DE MAR | ORMER, ABALONE

Gal: orella, peneira
Bas: itxas belarri
Cat: orella de mar

Por: orelha marinha
Fre: ormeau
Ger: Seeohr

Max <> 10; the largest single-shell mollusc found in Iberian markets. The inside of the shell is pearly, the outside grey or green and rough. Many of the common names refer to the resemblance between shell and ear, while a few allude rather to the row of holes in the shell. It is remarkable how many and various the vernacular names are. Besides the two Galician ones given above, Sueiro offers nine others, including zapatiño da Virxe and cuncha das señoras.

The large white adductor muscle is what is eaten. It often needs to be tenderized first. Best in August and September, according to Galicians.

Family PATELLIDAE
Patella spp
LAPA   LIMPET

Gal: alapa, cuco etc
Bas: lapa
Cat: barretet
Por: lapa
Fre: patelle
Ger: Schusselmuschel

Limpets vary in size but are rarely over 7 cm across and usually less. *Patella caerulea*, the species shown, is a common one.

    Limpets are edible but tend to be tough and are not often seen in the markets. They can be eaten raw, or cooked in a soup, or 'roasted' upside down with a little butter or oil.

Family TROCHIDAE
Monodonta turbinata
CARACOL GRIS,   TOP-SHELL
CARAMUJO, PEONTA

Gal: /
Bas: /
Cat: baldufa
Por: /
Fre: bigorneau
Ger: /

Max <> 3. A mollusc of the Mediterranean, as is its close relation *M articulata*. (There are lots of other top-shells in the Mediterranean, which may occasionally be found in local markets and some of these have ranges which extend into the Atlantic too. The French name escargot de mer, which simply means 'sea snail', may be used of any such creatures.)

Bolinus (formerly *Murex*) *brandaris*

CAÑADILLA   MUREX

Gal: /
Bas: murex ärantzaduna
Cat: cornet amb pues
Por: buzio
Fre: rocher épineux
Ger: Stachelschnecke

Size up to 9 cm, which also applies to its close relation shown on the lower part of the page; whereas another relation (not shown) *Ocenebra erinaceus*, is rather smaller.

Of the three species, all with a range throughout the Mediterranean, only the last has a distribution extending north of Portugal in the Atlantic.

The murex shells were famous in classical antiquity as the source of the Tyrian purple dye, and the Latin name murex apparently survives not only in Italian (murice, which is also an alternative Spanish name) but also in the Provençal burez.

Appreciated as food, the creatures are usually cooked in seasoned water until ready to be winkled out of their shells.

Phyllonotus (formerly *Murex*) *trunculus*

BUSANO   MUREX

Gal: /
Bas: /
Cat: cornet
Por: búzio
Fre: rocher à pourpre
Ger: Purpurschnecke

Family LACUNIDAE
Littorina littorea

BIGARO, CARACOLILLO WINKLE

Gal: caramuxo, mincha
Bas: karrakela, magurio
Cat: caragolí
Por: caramujo, burrié
Fre: bigorneau
Ger: Strandschnecke

Max <> 2.5, colour variable.

Winkles are usually boiled in their shells and then picked out with pins or special little forks (such as I once bought in Bilbao).

Family APORRHAIDAE
Aporrhais pespelicani

PIE DE PELÍCANO   PELICAN FOOT

Gal: /
Bas: /
Cat: /
Por: bandeira
Fre: pied de pélican
Ger: Pelikanfuss

Maximum dimensions just over 6 x 4 cm. Not common in the markets. The species *A serresianus* is similar but with more 'toes'.

If you can imagine removing the webbed foot from the pelican foot, what you would have left would be similar to one of the horn-shells of the family Cerithiidae, Spanish **pada**, sometimes marketed. *Cerithium vulgatum* is shown on the following page, top left.

To the right of that is a bonnet shell, *Cassidaria echinophora*, of the family Cascidae. It is **casco** in Spanish, may be up to 12 cm in length, and is occasionally marketed.

The far right-hand drawing shows one more single shell, of the family Cymatiidae: *Charonia rubicunda*, the knobbed triton, Spanish **caracola** or **bocina**, usually rather too tough and strong-tasting to be appreciated, especially if large (max <> 40).

Family BUCCINIDAE
Buccinum undatum

CARACOLA, BOCINA   WHELK

Gal: /
Bas: bukzino
Cat: /
Por: búzio
Fre: buccin
Ger: Wellhornschnecke

Max <> 15, mkt <> 6–9. This whelk is an Atlantic species. The one usually found in the Mediterranean is the smaller *Buccinulum corneum*, shown in the lower drawing; the Spanish name for it is **caracolillo**.

Whelks are predatory creatures, equipped with strong lips and rasping tongues which enable them to overcome other molluscs and suck their flesh out of their shells.

Although whelks are edible, they are not in great demand (and in some places liable to be toxic in certain conditions, and then to remain toxic for a long time). They are prepared for consumption by being boiled, after which they can be got out of their shells.

BIVALVES

The bivalves live in double, hinged shells, which they can open and close by means of a strong adductor muscle. They should be marketed alive, and it is usual to see a heap of them in a basket opening and closing their shells – and to avoid buying any which are in a permanently open or 'gaping' position, since they must be dead. But some, such as the razor shells, cannot close their shells completely.

The name 'clam' should, strictly speaking, be reserved for the bivalves which can fully close; but this rule is not always followed (for example, razor shells may be referred to as razor clams).

Advice to let bivalves 'purge' themselves by resting in clean sea water for a while is generally sound, in relation to those gathered from the wild. Those which are 'farmed', especially oysters, arrive at the market ready for consumption.

Family OSTREIDAE
Ostrea edulis
OSTRA (PLANA)   (EUROPEAN) OYSTER

Gal: ostra
Bas: ostra arrunt
Cat: ostra
Por: ostra redonda/fêmea/plana*
Fre: huître (plate)
Ger: Auster

Max <> 12, mkt <> 7–10; shape variable, colour usually grey, shell may be encrusted with traces of marine worms etc.

Oysters are usually eaten raw, with just a dash of lemon juice. Cooked oyster dishes are sometimes served, if supplies are plentiful and cheap; but I have not myself come across such dishes in Spain or Portugal, although I have seen recipes for Fried Oysters, Oysters 'en Escabeche', Oyster Pasties, etc.

* Another Portuguese name which can be applied both to this species and to the Portuguese oyster (next page) is carcanhola (and, for small specimens, maranhão).

Crassostrea gigas (= *C angulata*)

OSTIÓN, OSTRA PORTUGUESA

PORTUGUESE OYSTER

Gal: ostra portuguesa
Bas: ostratzar
Cat: ostra portuguesa
Por: ostra portuguesa
Fre: portugaise
Ger: portugiesische Auster

Max <> 25, mkt <> highly variable, usually about 10.

It has recently been declared that the species for long recognized under the names *Crassostrea angulata* and 'Portuguese oyster' is in fact identical with *Crassostrea gigas*, the oriental oyster, hitherto treated as a separate and larger species. As *C gigas* was named earlier than *C angulata*, its name prevails. However, most books still reflect what had been standard practice until recently.

The Portuguese oyster has natural habitats on parts of the Portuguese coast and at the head of the Adriatic and some other places, but has gained much wider importance as a result of its introduction in other parts to replace the less robust *Ostrea edulis*.

To quote something else I wrote: 'The story has often been told of how a ship called the *Morlaisien* had to shelter in the Gironde during stormy weather in the 1860s; how her cargo of Portuguese oysters, having spoiled, was thrown overboard; and how those oysters which were still alive found the *eaux limoneuses* of the Gironde perfectly to their liking and multiplied. It is a characteristic of the Portuguese oyster to be adaptable.'

The quality of the Portuguese oyster is generally considered to be less good than that of *Ostrea edulis*. However, good 'Portuguese' can be very good. What was said on the preceding page about serving oysters applies to this species also.

Mytilus galloprovincialis, M edulis
MEJILLÓN   MUSSEL

Gal: mexillón
Bas: muskuilu
Cat: musclo
Por: mexilhão,
Fre: moule
Ger: Miesmuschel

Max <> 10, mkt <> 5–7. *Mytilus edulis* is the best known and most common European mussel; it has a wide distribution in the Atlantic and is also present in the Mediterranean. *M galloprovincialis* is the Mediterranean mussel, formerly counted as just a variety of *M edulis* but now treated as a separate species.

Spain is the most prominent country of western and southern Europe in myticulture, as the culture of mussels is called. This eminence has been achieved by adopting the technique of myticulture on ropes suspended from rafts in suitable waters, of which those in the numerous deep bays of the Galician coast are ideal.

Stuffed baked mussels (Mejillones Rellenos) occur in various forms. Mejillones Tigre are with guindillas (little red chilli peppers). In Portugal Sopa de Camarão e Mexhilhões, a soup of shrimp and mussels, is popular.

Another species which may be met in Spanish and Portuguese markets is *Modiolus barbatus*, the bearded horse mussel, shown at the foot of the page, on the left. In the far south of Spain one may also meet *Perna picta* (Spanish, **mejillón africano**), shown bottom right.

Family MYTILIDAE
Lithophaga lithophaga
DATIL DE MAR   DATE-SHELL

Gal: /
Bas: /
Cat: dàtil de mar
Por. /
Fre: datte de mer
Ger: Seedattel

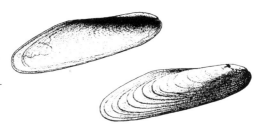

Max <> around 10, the same as the mussel; but this is a slimmer creature which embeds itself in rocks and is not easy to harvest.

Some say that it makes a better soup than the regular mussel. It can also be eaten raw, provided that the provenance is safe.

Family PINNIDAE
Pinna nobilis
NACÁR   FAN MUSSEL

Gal: /	*Por:* funil, pinha marinha
Bas: nakar	*Fre:* jambonneau
Cat: nacre	*Ger:* /

A large bivalve: max 75, mkt <> 30–40. The adductor muscle, as in the case of the scallop, can be extracted and cooked.

Pecten maximus

VIEIRA, CONCHA PEREGRINA/ DE PEREGRINO

(PILGRIM) SCALLOP

Gal: vieira, aviñeira
Bas: beira handi
Cat: petxina de pelegri

Por: vieira, romeira
Fre: coquille Saint-Jacques
Ger: (grosse) Kammuschel

Spain and Portugal have two large scallops, of which this one (max <> 16, mkt <> around 9) is essentially an Atlantic species; whereas the very slightly smaller *P jacobaeus*, shown on the right, belongs mainly to the Mediterranean (and I am told that even there it is uncommon in the western basin and probably does not occur naturally on Spain's Mediterranean coast). The easiest way of distinguishing the two is to remember that the ribs on the shell of *P jacobaeus* are flattened, whereas those of *P maximus* are rounded (as shown in the drawings). Both species have about 16 such ribs.

Common names for these two large scallops are more or less the same. It is, however, *P maximus* which has a special religious significance, since its shell has for very many centuries been the badge worn by pilgrims to the shrine of Saint James at Santiago de Compostela in Galicia. (The connection has become so well established that some people even believe that pilgrim scallops are only found in Galician waters. In fact their range extends from Portugal up to Norway. However, it is true that they are especially good in Galicia.)

Scallops, whether these large species or the smaller ones described on the next page, are greatly prized as food. The white adductor muscle, which is what enables them to snap their shells open and shut and thus propel themselves through the water, is the main edible part, together with the coral, which may be surprisingly large.

Vieiras Rellenas (or Santiaguesas) is a dish of large scallops baked in their shells with breadcrumbs, ham, onion and wine. I find it somewhat coarse myself; the delicate flavour of scallop meat can easily be overwhelmed by onion and its texture difficult to enjoy under a thick crust of breadcrumbs.

Family PECTINIDAE

Chlamys varia

ZAMBURIÑA   SCALLOP

Gal: zamburiña   *Por:* vieira da pedra
Bas: zamburiña   *Fre:* pétoncle
Cat: petxina variada   *Ger:* /

Mkt <> around 5. This species, shown below left, has about 30 ribs on the shell.

Both this smaller scallop and the one described below belong to the group which have two equally rounded shells (in contrast to the larger species on the preceding page, which have one flat and one rounded shell).

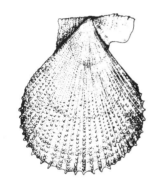 

Chlamys opercularis

VOLANDEIRA   QUEEN

Gal: anduriña,   *Por:* vieira
samoriña portuguese   *Fre:* vanneau
Bas: bolandeira   *Ger:* /
Cat: xel, xelet

The other common scallop of about this size, shown above right, has about 20 ribs.

Family GLYCYMERIDAE
Glycymeris glycymeris

ALMENDRA DE MAR   DOG-COCKLE

Gal: rabioso
Bas: itsas arbendola
Cat: petxinot
Por: castanhola
Fre: amande de mer
Ger: Sammetemuschel

Max <> 7. The outside of the shell is prettily marked by radiating and concentric lines.

May be eaten raw, but is not tender. It is fairly well known on the Iberian coasts and in the Bay of Biscay, but attracts less attention elsewhere.

The closely related *G violacascens*, **almeja tonta**, is brought to the market in some places, often mixed with the main species; it tends to violet in coloration.

Family CARDIIDAE
Acanthocardia tuberculata

LANGOSTILLO,   COCKLE
BERBERECHO VERRUCOSO

Gal: (berberecho) marolo   *Por:* berbigão burro
Bas: berberetxo garatxodun   *Fre:* bucarde
Cat: petxina puntxenta   *Ger:* /

A tuberculata   *A aculeata*   *A echinata*

Max <> 9, mkt <> 5–7. This species, as the specific name *tuberculata* indicates, has tubercles on its shell.

A aculeata (max <> 10) has prickly spines: Spanish **marolo**. The animal inside is vermilion in colour, an arresting sight.

A echinata (max <> 6.5) has blunt prickles: Spanish **berberecho espinoso**; Galician berberecho macho or croque bravo.

Family CARDIIDAE
Cerastoderma glaucum
BERBERECHO (VERDE), VERDIGÓN   COCKLE

Gal: birollo, berberecho
Bas: berberetxo berde
Cat: escopinya de gallet
Por: berbigão
Fre: coque (glauque)
Ger: Herzmuschel

Mkt <> 3–4. Colour olive green. A species of both the Mediterranean and the Atlantic.

This and the species below are eaten raw or steamed open in a court-bouillon. It is said to be advisable to let them stand in salt water for a few hours before eating or cooking them, the idea being that they can then disgorge sand etc. Same treatment as for clams.

Cerastoderma edule
BERBERECHO   COCKLE

Gal: berberecho, croque
Bas: berberetxo arrunt, margola
Cat: escopinya de gallet
Por: berbigão
Fre: coque
Ger: Herzmuschel

Max <> 5, mkt <> 3–4. This very similar species is rarely found in the Mediterranean, and then only in the west, but is common in the Atlantic.

Cockles were not much sought after in the first half of the 20th century, but demand increased dramatically in the second half and overfishing took place, to such an extent that in the early 1970s the Spanish authorities had to impose in Galicia and later elsewhere a system of concessions; these are stretches of shore where the people who have bought the concessions have sole rights to gather cockles. Armed guards have to be posted on some concessions to deter cockle-poachers. The cockle 'beds' are 'seeded' to increase productivity, and anxious thought is given to protecting the molluscs from crustacean predators such as the African fiddler crab (page 141).

Venus verrucosa

VERIGUETO, WARTY VENUS
ESCUPIÑA GRABADA

Gal: carneiro
Bas: txirla garatxodun
Cat: escopinya gravada
Por: pé de burro
Fre: praire
Ger: rauhe Venusmuschel

Max <> 6; always strongly ridged and usually yellowish grey.

Often eaten raw; or used in seafood soups, or steamed open to be eaten with pasta (the Italian name for this and the two species below, is vongola).

Chamelea (formerly *Venus*) *gallina*

CHIRLA STRIPED VENUS

Gal: chirla
Bas: /
Cat: rossellona
Por: pé de burrinho
Fre: petite praire
Ger: Venusmuschel

Max <> 5, mkt <> 2.5–3.5, so slightly smaller than the preceding species.

The chirla (a name which, incidentally, is sometimes applied to other species in other places) is of fair quality. It may be used like the preceding species.

Dosinia exoleta

ALMEJÓN REDONDO, (NO ENGLISH NAME)
RELOJ

Gal: moelo, reloxito
Bas: /
Cat: almejón real
Por: ameixola redonda
Fre: coque plate
Ger: /

Max <> 6, mkt <> 4–5. Of inferior quality, usually consigned to use in conserved form, rather than being sold fresh.

Family VENERIDAE
Ruditapes decussatus (= Venerupis decussata, Tapes decussatus)
ALMEJA FINA CARPET-SHELL

Gal: ameixa fina
Bas: txirla (handia)
Cat: cloïssa (fina)
Por: amêijoa boa
Fre: palourde
Ger: Teppichmuschel

Max <> 8; marked by fine lines in both directions, ie around the shell and also fanning out from the hinge. Greatly appreciated in France.

In the north of Spain a species introduced from the orient, *Tapes philippinarum* (Spanish **almeja japonesa**, Galician, ameija xaponesa) is being 'farmed'.

Venerupis pullastra (= Tapes pullastra)
ALMEJA BABOSA, CHOCHA (VENUS SHELL)

Gal: ameixa babosa/macha
Bas: /
Cat: /
Por: amêijoa macha
Fre: poulette, coque bleue
Ger: /

Max <> 7, mkt <> 4. Colour is variable – cream, grey, brownish – with variable darker markings often in the form of zigzags.

Some think this clam better than the almeja fina; but it does not live as long out of the water, so is less common in inland markets.

Venerupis aurea (= Tapes aureus)
ALMEJA DORADA/ GOLDEN CARPET-
MARGARITA SHELL

Gal: ameixa bruxa/bicuda
Bas: urre-txirla
Cat: margarida
Por: ameixoa
Fre: clovisse (jaune)
Ger: /

Max <> 5. Not always golden in colour – may be orange or even have a violet tinge. In some places it may be called almeja blanca.

Delicious; and well suited by its small size to being eaten with pasta or the like. Almejas con Arroz (with rice) is well known; and Fabes con Almejas (broad beans with almejas) is popular in Asturias.

Family VENERIDAE
Callista chione

ALMEJÓN BRILLANTE, SAVERINA   SMOOTH VENUS

Gal: ameixón, ameixa macha
Bas: txirla arre gorriska
Cat: petxinot lluenta/de sang
Por: concha fina
Fre: verni
Ger: braune Venusmuschel

Max <> 12 across, so quite a large clam. The polished, almost 'varnished', surface of the shell accounts for many of the common names. Colour varies, but is usually light brown, with broken bands of a darker colour radiating outwards.

Good eating, raw or cooked.

Family DONACIDAE
Donax trunculus

COQUINA, TALLARINA   WEDGE SHELL

Gal: coquiña, arola
Bas: kadeluxa
Cat: tellerina
Por: conquilha, cadelinha
Fre: olive, haricot de mer
Ger: Sägezänchen

A small clam – max <> not quite 4 – whose shell is shaped something like a wedge. Colour, which varies, is often purplish or tawny. This species is the best known of the genus, but there are others (eg *D vittatus*), and there are also some quite similar species in other genera of the family Tellinidae.

Often used in soups, eg the Italian Zuppa di Telline. In Spain, especially on the southern coasts, where they abound, they are highly rated despite their small size.

Family MACTRIDAE
Mactra corallina (formerly *M stultorum*)
ALMEJA LISA   TROUGH-SHELL

Gal: ameixola
Bas: txirla leun
Cat: petxina llisa
Por: ameijóla
Fre: blanchet
Ger: Trogmuschel

Max <> 7, mkt <> around 5. This trough-shell, marketed quite often in Italy but not so much elsewhere, is one of several, all edible. Another, which belongs to the Atlantic, is *Spisula solida* (= *Mactra solida*), **almeja blanca** in Spanish, cornicha in Galician, related to but smaller than the well-known surf clam of North America.

Lutraria lutraria
AROLA   OTTER SHELL

Gal: arola, navallón
Bas: /
Cat: ou, navalló
Por: faca
Fre: lutraire
Ger: Trogmuschel

Max <> 13, mkt <> 9–10. This creature lives fairly deep down in the sand, with only its long siphon protruding. It is sometimes met in the markets, but not in great demand. The same applies to close relations such as *L magna* (formerly *oblonga*) and *L angustior*.

Family SCROBICULARIIDAE
Scrobicularia plana (= *S piperata*)
ALMEJA DE PERRO, CADELA   FURROW SHELL

Gal: cadela (de mar/de frade)
Bas: txirla zapal
Cat: cloïssa plana
Por: lambujinha
Fre: lavignon
Ger: Pfeffermuschel

Market length 4–5 cm. Whitish or anyway pale in colour, peppery in taste.

Ensis ensis

(1)   **NAVAJA**   **RAZOR-SHELL**

Gal: navalla   *Por:* longueirão
Bas: datil oker   *Fre:* couteau
Cat: navalla   *Ger:* Schwertmuschel

Ensis siliqua

(2)   **MUERGO**   **RAZOR-SHELL**

Gal: navalla, longueirón   *Por:* longueirão
Bas: datil handi   *Fre:* couteau
Cat: /   *Ger:* /

Solen marginatus (formerly *S vagina*)

(3)   **LONGUEIRÓN,**   **RAZOR-SHELL**
    NAVAJA RUGOSA

Gal: longueirón vello   *Por:* faca
Bas: itsas datil, datil ildoduna   *Fre:* couteau
Cat: ganivet, mànec   *Ger:* Messeerscheide

(1)
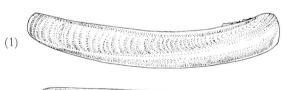

(2)

(3)

Max <> 17, mkt <> about 9 or 10. The razor-shells are all edible, and make very good soups. The common names often overlap; thus muergo may be used of (1) and (3) as well as (2), and morguera may be used of (2) or (3), while the Galician name navalla and a corresponding Portuguese name navalha may apply to any of them.

Family GLOSSIDAE

Glossus humanus (formerly *Isocardia cor*)

CORAZÓN DE BUEY   HEART-COCKLE

Gal: reló
Bas: idi biotz
Cat: /
Por: /
Fre: coeur de boeuf
Ger: /

Mkt <> 6–7 cm; but not often seen for sale, as not greatly esteemed.

Family PHOLADIDAE

Pholas dactylus

FOLADO   PIDDOCK

Gal: folada, broca
Bas: txirla barrenari
Cat: peus de cabra
Por: taralhão
Fre: pholade
Ger: Bohrmuschel

Max <> 15, mkt <> half of that. The shells, typically whitish or pale grey/yellow outside, gape noticeably at both ends and have serrated edges for part of their length.

Two alternative French names, religieuse and bonne-soeur, have been bestowed because the piddock is supposed to look like a nun's head-dress in shape.

Piddocks create their own dwellings (or, one might say, prisons) by boring into sand, mud, wood, or rock, especially limestone. They are rarely seen in the markets, but edible – or of use as bait.

CEPHALOPODS

The term 'cephalopods' means 'feet-in-mouths'. All these creatures have tentacles; all offer a high proportion of edible flesh; and all are prized in both Spain and Portugal. Some of those marketed come from far away, since the fishery for squid, in particular, has become a global affair. They freeze well and their bodily characteristic make it easy to stow a lot of them in a small space.

Family SEPIIDAE
Sepia officinalis

JIBIA   CUTTLEFISH

Gal: xiba, choco   *Por:* choco
Bas: txoko   *Fre:* seiche
Cat: sípia, sèpia   *Ger:* Sepia

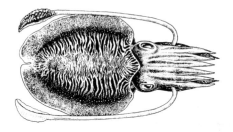

Max body <> 25 , mkt <> 12–16. The colour of the back is dark with markings such as those shown in the drawing.

Cuttlefish of much smaller size are often seen in the markets; these could be infant specimens of this species but are more likely to belong to the two different species which are listed below and at the top of the next page; or be members of the family Sepiolidae, also on the next page.

Cuttlefish can be cut up (after cleaning) and fried, or stuffed and stewed. Very small ones are best deep-fried.

Cuttlefish have ink, like squid, but less of it and less intensely black; the ink of the cuttlefish is considered to be ideal for the dish Arroz Negro (black rice).

FIRST SMALL RELATION: *Sepia elegans*

CASTAÑO, CHOQUITO   LITTLE CUTTLEFISH

Castanyó in Catalan. Of a yellowish hue.

SECOND SMALL RELATION: *Sepia orbignyana*
CHOPITO   LITTLE CUTTLEFISH

Sepia de punxa in Catalan; choco in Portuguese. Pale red-brown in colour.

Family SEPIOLIDAE
Sepiola rondeleti
CHIPIRÓN   LITTLE CUTTLEFISH

Gal: /	*Por:* chopo
Bas: /	*Fre:* sépiole
Cat: /	*Ger:* Zwergsepia

The Sepiolidae have internal 'bones' made of chitin, and they are all small. *Sepiola rondeleti*, shown below left, is merely one of about a dozen species of little 'bobtail', to adopt the English name used by the FAO for *Sepiola* and closely related genera.

Delicious morsels, which are so small (bodies about 2 cm long) that they can be cooked without cleaning. Chipirones en su Tinta (with their ink) are a favourite Spanish dish.

Rossia macrosoma
CHOCO, GLOBITO   (LITTLE) CUTTLEFISH

Gal: chopiño, choquiño	*Por:* chopo
Bas: /	*Fre:* sepiole
Cat: /	*Ger:* Zwergsepia

Shown above, right. Slightly larger than the *Sepiola* spp, body length 3-6 cm.

Loligo vulgaris

CALAMAR, PUNTILLA   SQUID

Gal: lula, lura   *Por:* lula
Bas: txibia, txipiroi (small)   *Fre:* encornet
Cat: calamarsó   *Ger:* Kalmar

The usual market length of this, the common squid, is around 15–25 cm, but its maximum length is 40 cm. The closely similar species *L forbesi* is larger, but much less common in Iberian waters. A medium-sized species (mkt <> 7–12) which is common in the Atlantic and West Mediterranean is *Alloteuthis media*. A close relation, shown below in both male and female forms, is *A subulata*, which lacks the long tentacles possessed by its brother. Both these species may be called puntilla, lura, chipirón or calamarín.

I should mention that squid are among the categories of seafood which are nowadays being brought back to Spain from distant waters; so one may well find in the markets some species which have not been listed here.

Squid are good to eat, and are especially suitable for being stuffed (Calamares Rellenos) – the cleaned body providing a ready-made bag into which the stuffing (which may include the chopped tentacles) can go. Calamares en su Tinta are cooked with their own 'ink' (the same applies to chipirones). Arroz Negro is a rice dish coloured black with the same ink (but see page 162). Calamares a la Romana are sliced into rings, battered and fried. Squid are also tasty when stewed with wine, tomato, onion, olive oil etc.

The flying squid, treated on the next page, are considered to be inferior fare.

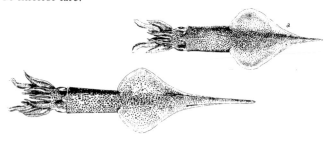

Illex coindetii

VOLADOR, POTA FLYING SQUID
VOLADORA

Gal: lura, pota, choupa   *Por:* pota
Bas: /   *Fre:* calmar
Cat: canana   *Ger:* Pfeilkalmar

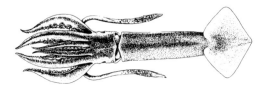

Max <> 27 (of females, males are smaller), mkt <> 15–22.

This flying squid is common in the Atlantic and the Mediterranean. It may be confused with another species, *Todaropsis sagittatus*, which is larger, especially in the Atlantic; or with the smaller *T eblanae*, Spanish **pota costera**. *T sagittatus*, which is shown below, is **pota** or **aluda** in Spanish.

Flying squid do not really fly, but can propel themselves out of the water and glide through the air for some distance.

Generally, flying squid are thought to be less good to eat than squid; but among them *Illex coindetii* is to be preferred.

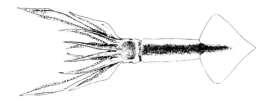

Family OCTOPODIDAE
Octopus vulgaris
PULPO   OCTOPUS

Gal: polbo
Bas: olagarro
Cat: pop
Por: polvo
Fre: pieuvre
Ger: Octopus

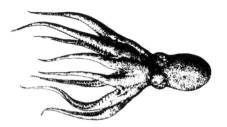

What is the plural of the English word octopus? A vexed question. It cannot be octopi nor octopodes; and octopuses looks awkward, so octopus it must be.

There are giant octopus, but they are not common. Normally, a large octopus will only measure 40 to 100 cm overall (ie including head and tentacles). O *vulgaris*, which is the best species, has two rows of suckers along its tentacles.

The flesh of an octopus may need to be tenderized before cooking. Beating the creature on rocks is one favoured technique. Others put a large cork in the cooking water.

Empanada de Pulpo (Galician octopus pie) is one of several excellent Spanish octopus dishes; another is Pulpo a la Gallega (boiled, then served cold with a dressing of olive oil and paprika). The northern coast of Spain provides a good habitat for these creatures, which are appreciated throughout Spain, but especially in Galicia (where special octopus cooks turn up with huge copper pots in which to cook octopus at fairs and feasts).

The Portuguese enjoy Polvo com Arroz, octopus with rice.

There is a close relation, *Octopus macropus*, the white-spotted octopus, **pulpo patudo** in Spanish, which is found all round the world but rarely in the Mediterranean. The body is brown, with white spots ('mousse au chocolat garnie de crème fraîche', said one naturalist).

Another octopus, *Eledone cirrosa*, the 'horned' or 'curled' octopus, is shown on the right. It is small, and light in colour, so **pulpo blanco** in Spanish and pop blanc in Catalan, but polvo de alto (deep water octopus) in Portuguese. Young specimens are preferred for eating.

MISCELLANEOUS SEA CREATURES

The catalogue ends with four oddities, all outside the realms of fish, crustaceans and molluscs, and all shown on the next two pages.

Before introducing them, I should explain that some creatures which might be expected to figure here are absent, for the simple reason that the idea of eating them is no longer acceptable. This applies especially to marine mammals. It is well known that the dolphin, famed since classical antiquity for its friendly attitude towards human beings, was regarded almost everywhere (an exception being the port of Genoa) as immune to the attentions of fishermen. And many people now feel that the whale should enjoy a similar protected status.

The situation of sea turtles is less in the public eye, and the case for leaving them alone, although less dependent on emotional considerations which apply to mammals, does rest on one related ground; the danger of extinction. When I wrote *Mediterranean Seafood* 20 years ago, this problem was already clear for one species which occurs in the Mediterranean; but now it seems to involve other species too.

This said, we can inspect with a clear conscience the creatures which have not been discarded on such grounds. Of them, the sea urchin is a real delicacy, and acknowledged to be so from as far back as records go.

The second is also a great delicacy,, but counts as a very recent arrival in European gastronomy – and one for which Spain deserves all the credit. This strange creature is well known in the orient as bêche de mer (a French name, which has stuck because some species are plentiful in French islands in the Pacific) or under Chinese names (the Chinese being the greatest enthusiasts for them). But this Mediterranean species passed almost unnoticed until recently, when a restaurateur in Barcelona, knowing that fishermen further down the coast ate it with pleasure, put it on his menu – with sensational results, since it now ranks as just about the most costly seafood available. The Spanish manage to take from them small fillets which are not gelatinous (like the Chinese product) but firm and tasty. Highly recommended, specially at the Botafumeiro restaurant in Barcelona, where they are served in four different ways.

The last two entries in the cagalogue are among those delicacies which are well liked by those who like them; but the number of such people is limited.

Family ECHINIDAE
Paracentrotus lividus

ERIZO DE MAR   SEA URCHIN

Gal: ourizo de mar
Bas: itsas triku (arrunt)
Cat: eriçó/garota de roca
Por: ouriço do mar
Fre: oursin
Ger: Seeigel

Diameter of 'test' up to 6 cm. The orange roes of these prickly creatures, reached by cutting off the top half of the 'test' (preferably with a special implement, known in France as a 'coupe-oursin') are eaten raw with a dash of lemon juice and are greatly appreciated – especially in Asturias, says one Spanish authority.

There is another species, *Sphaerechinus granularis*, called in Spanish **erizo violáceo** because of its violet colour.

Alternative Castilian names for either of these sea urchins are oricio, castaño de mar.

Family STICHOPODIDAE
Stichopus regalis

COHOMBRO   SEA CUCUMBER

Gal: /
Bas: itsas luzoker
Cat: espardenya
Por: holotúria
Fre: holothurie
    (Provence: pantuflo)
Ger: Holothurie

Max <> 35, mkt <> 25. Distribution of this primitive-looking creature extends from the Bay of Biscay all the way round to Sicily. See the preceding page for its 'discovery' in Spanish waters.

Family ACTINIDAE
Anemonia sulcata

ORTIGA DE MAR, ORTIGUILLA

SEA ANEMONE

Gal: /	Por: anémona de mar
Bas: (itsas) anemona	Fre: ortie de mer
Cat: /	Ger: /

It is hard to know how to measure the size of these creatures; anyway, they are not very big and not seen much in the markets. But their delicate flavour is appreciated in Andalucia, where they are eaten fried; and they can be used to make a seafood soup.

Family PYURIDAE
Microcosmus sulcatus

PROBECHO

SEA SQUIRT

Gal: /	Por: /
Bas: /	Fre: violet, figue de mer
Cat: /	Ger: Mikrokosmos

The maximum dimension is over 20 cm. It is the yellow part inside which is eaten raw, something like scrambled egg in appearance.

SEAFOOD FROM DISTANT WATERS

Besides traditional imports such as bacalao, which I have mentioned in this book. Spain and Portugal are now consuming various species which were unknown in their markets two or three decades ago, Many are the result of fishing in distant waters by Spanish or Portuguese fishing vessels. Modern techniques for freezing catches at sea permit them to bring back not just cured fish, as they have done for many centuries, but also freshly frozen fish.

This is not all. Cargo aircraft can bring to them, as to other European countries, fresh seafood from other continents, provided that its value is high enough to absorb the cost of air freight.

All these activities have, in a beneficial but sometimes bewildering way, complicated the scene in seafood markets and threaten the claim of any guide such as the present one to be fully comprehensive.

However, the complications are less than might be supposed. On the whole, it is true to say, and not surprising, that the 'new' species brought to Spain and Portugal are close relations of species already well liked, and have been chosen for precisely that reason.

To take one set of examples, the beloved hake has close relations in other oceans, comparable in size and quality; and it now makes commercial sense to import some of them. The excellent reference book produced by FROM (see bibliography) lists and illustrates ten 'other hake'. Six of these belong to the same genus (*Merluccius*) as the true hake; thus *M hubbsi* is 'Argentine hake', and *M capensis* is 'Cape hake'. Others, however, belong to other genera.

Substitutes for true bacalao include *Gadus odac*, 'Greenland cod', *G macrocephalus*, **bacalao de Alaska**; and a Chilean fish of another genus, known as **bacalao criollo**.

The prized angler-fish of Iberian waters has a rival in *Luphius upsicephalus*, 'Cape angler-fish'. And appreciation of the Spanish gallineta (page 98) has been enough to create interest in relations from far away, such as *Sebastes alutus*, **gallineta del Pacifico**.

All this applies also, and perhaps even more so, to groups such as prawns. These include large species which can be farmed in, for example, S E Asia and which are sufficiently valuable to be transported to markets in Europe or North America. When they turn up in Spanish markets they have names which reflect their origins (**langostino mexicano, langostino de Guinea, gambón argentino**) or say something about their appearance (**langostino banana/blanco/jumbo**).

BIBLIOGRAPHY

Adema, J P H M: *Krabben van Nederland en Belgie:* Leiden, Nationaal Natuurhistorisch Museum, 1991

Albuquerque, Rolanda Maria: *Peixes de Portugal e ilhas adjacentes*, originally published in *Portugaliae Acta Biologica* (B), vol V, Lisbon, 1954-6.

Alonso, Eliseo: *Pescadores del río Miño:* Pontevedra, Diputación Provincial, 1989.

Arbex, Juan Carlos: *Pescadores Españoles*, vols I-II: Madrid, Ministerio de Agricultura, Pesca y Alimentación, 1990.

Bianchi, Gabriella: *Des Ressources Halieutiques de l'Atlantique Marocain:* Rome, FAO, 1984.

Bianchi, Gabriella: *Espécies Comerciais Marinhas e de Águas Salobras de Angola:* Rome, FAO, 1986.

Bini, Giorgio: *Atlante dei Pesci delle Coste Italiane*, vols I-VIII: Rome, Mondo Sommerso, 1960-70.

Calera, Ana María: *La Cocina Vasca:* Bilbao, La Gran Enciclopedia Vasca, 1971.

Camba, Julio: *La Casa de Lúculo, o El Arte de Comer*, 6th edn: Madrid, Espasa-Calpe, 1961.

Capel, José Carlos: *Manual del Pescado:* Madrid, Penthalon, 1982.

Castejon, Luis Gallego: *Vertebrados Ibericos, 1: 'Peces':* Seville, published by the author, 1978.

Collette, Bruce B & Nauen, Cornelia E: *Scombrids of the World* (FAO Species Catalogue, vol 2): Rome, FAO, 1983.

Compagno, Leonard J V: *Sharks of The World*, pts 1 & 2, (FAO Species Catalogue, vol 4): Rome, FAO, 1984.

Cornide, Don Joseph: *Ensayo de una Historia de los Peces y Otras Producciones Marinas de la Costa de Galicia:* La Coruña, 1983 (facsimile of original published at Madrid, 1788).

Davidson, Alan: *A Kipper with my Tea:* London, Macmillan, 1988 and Berkeley CA, North Point Press, 1989.

Davidson, Alan: *Mediterranean Seafood*, 2nd edn: London, Allen Lane and Penguin Books, 1981.

Davidson, Alan: *North Atlantic Seafood*, 2nd edn: London, Penguin Books, 1981.

Davidson, Alan: *On Fasting and Feasting* (an anthology): London, Macdonald, 1988.

De Juana, E & A R de Juana, A: *Guía de Pescados y Mariscos de Consumo usual en España*, 2nd edn: Barcelona, Ediciones Omega, 1987.

De Luna, José Carlos: *Peces de los Litorales Iberico y Marroqui y su Pesca deportiva:* Madrid, 1948.

FAO (Food and Agriculture Organization of the United Nations): *Species Identification Sheets for the Mediterranean and the Black Sea,* vols 1 & 2: Rome, FAO, 1987.

FROM (former institution of the Spanish Ministry of Agriculture etc): *Catalogo de Denominaciones de Especies Acuícolas Españolas:* Madrid, Ministry of Agriculture etc, 1985.

FROM (see preceding entry): *Catalogo de Denominaciones de Especies Acuícolas Fortaneas: Peces, Crustaceos, Móluscos:* Madrid, Ministry of Agriculture etc, 1986.

Gomez Caruana, F & Diaz Luna, J L: *Guía de los Peces continentales de la Peninsula Iberica:* Madrid, Acción Divulgativa, 1991.

Holthuis, L B: *Shrimps and Prawns of the World* (FAO Species Catalogue, vol 1): Rome, FAO, 1980.

Lotina Bengurio, Roberto & Hormaechea Camiña, Mario de: *Peces de Mar y de Rio:* Bilbao, Asuri/Urmo, 1975.

Lozano, F: *Nomenclatura Ictiologica – Nombres Cientificos y Vulgares de los Peces Españoles:* Madrid, Istituto Español de Oceanografia, 1963.

Manjon, Maite: *Gastronomy of Spain and Portugal:* London, Garamond, 1990.

Ministerio de Agricultura, Pesca y Alimentación: *Los Pescados Azules de Nuestras Costas:* Madrid, 1985.

Muus, Bent J: *Skallus, Søtænder, Blæksprutter* (vol 65 of *Danmarks Fauna*, covering inter alia the cephalopods): Copenhagen, 1959.

Nuñes, Adao de Abreu: *Peixes da Madeira,* 2nd edn: Funchal, Junta Geral, 1974.

Ortiz, Elisabeth Lambert: *The Food of Spain and Portugal – The Complete Iberian Cuisine:* Oxford, Lennard Publishing, 1989.

Osório de Castro, Jerónimo De Melo: *Nomenclatura Portuguesa do Pescado:* Lisbon, Gabinete de Estudos das Pescas, 1967.

Ramonell, Rosa: *Guía dos Mariscos de Galicia:* Vigo, Galaxia, 1985.

Rios Panisse, Mª del Carmen Rios: *Nomenclatura de la Flora y Fauna Maritimas de Galicia, I Invertebrados y Peces* con Anotaciones Etimológicas por Antonio Santamarino: being *Verba* (Anuario Gallego de Filologia), Anejo 7: Universidad de Santiago de Compostela, 1977.

Salvador, Archiduque Luis: *Las Baleares - La Pesca* (recent reprint of part of the 1956 edition of a work written in 1880): Palma de Mallorca, Edicions Palma, 1983.

Sevilla, María José: *Life and Food in the Basque Country:* London, Weidenfeld & Nicolson, 1989.

Subsecretaría de la Marina mercante: *Nomenclatura oficial Española de los Animales marinos de Interes pesquero,* 2nd edn: Madrid, 1972.

Solórzano, Manuel Rodríguez; Regueiro, Sergio Devesa; Garrido, Lidia Soutullo: *Guía dos Peixes de Galicia:* Vigo, Galaxia, 1983.

Sueiro, Jorge-Victor: *El Libro del Marisco:* Madrid, Alianza Editorial, 1990.

U.Z.E.I. (Banco de Bilbao): *Biologia/1* - Landare eta Animalien Izenak, Izenegia: Donostia (San Sebastian), Ediciones Elkar, 1984 (and reprinted 1990).

Vélez, Carmen: *El Libro de los Pescados:* Madrid, Alianza Editorial, 1987.

Vieira, Edite: *The Taste of Portugal:* London, Robert Hale, 1988 (and later in paperback and in a Portuguese edn).

Villaverde, Luis: *Mariscos de Galicia* - como son, como viven, como se pescan y como se comen, Prologo y Notas al Texto de Valentin Paz-Andrade: La Coruña, Ediciones del Castro, 1974.

Villoch, Joaquín: *Guía de los Mariscos de los Mercados de Galicia:* La Coruña, Casa de las Ciencias, 1992

Villoch, Joaquín: *Guía de los Peces de las Lonjas de Galicia,* 2nd edn: La Coruña, Casa de las Ciencias, 1991

Vitorino, Gabriela: *Atlas Linguístico do Litoral Português - Fauna e Flora:* dissertation, Centro de Linguística da Universidade de Lisboa, Lisbon, 1987.

Whitehead, P J P et al: *Fishes of the North-eastern Atlantic and the Mediterranean,* vols I-III: Paris, UNESCO, 1984.

Wright, David & Patrick Swift: *Algarve:* London, Barrie & Jenkins, 1965.

This illustration shows how the goose-necked barnacle grows in clusters (see page 142).

SOURCES OF DRAWINGS

Producing drawings of fish and other seafood which are simultaneously 'diagnostic' (ie aiding recognition by showing clearly the various features used for this purpose) and 'artistic' (a pleasure to behold) is a specialized art. The outstanding collection of such drawings is that built up by the Food and Agriculture Organization of the United Nations (FAO, as it is generally known). Artists working at their headquarters in Rome over the last decade, illustrating the manifold Species Identification Sheets for Fishery Areas into which the oceans of the world are divided for this purpose, have created this collection; it is now a unique resource for all who are working with or writing about fish in any part of the world.

The FAO have kindly given permission for a very large number of these drawings, from the Species Identification Sheets for the Mediterranean and the Black Sea, to be reproduced in this book, notably:

for fish, those on pages 18, 20, 21, 23, 24, 25, 26, 27, 32, 33, 34, 35, 36, 37, 38, 39, 40, 41, 42, 43, 44, 45, 46, 47, 48, 49, 50, 51, 52, 53, 54, 55, 57, 58, 59, 60, 61, 62, 63, 64, 65, 66, 67, 68, 69, 70, 71, 72, 73, 74, 75, 76, 77, 78, 79, 80, 81, 82 (upper), 85 (upper), 87, 88, 92, 93, 94, 95, 96, 97, 98, 99 (upper), 100, 101, 102, 103, 104, 105, 106, 107, 108, 109, 110, 111, 112 (lower, also upper ex Angola), 113 (top and bottom), 114, 115, 116, 117, 118, 119, 120, 121, 122, 123, 124, 125, 126, 127

and for other forms of seafood, those on pages 128, 129 (left), 130, 131 (upper), 132, 133, 134, 135 (upper), 139 (first and second), 141 (lower), 142, 147 (top three and bottom), 150 (upper), 151, 152, 154 (bottom three), 155 (upper: also lower, Maroc), 156 (top, also Maroc), 158 (lower, also Maroc)

In addition, I have with permission used drawings from the FAO publication *Espécies Comercais Marinhas e de Aguas Salobras de Angola* (112, upper); and from the companion *Des Ressources Halieutiques de l'Atlantique Marocain* (155, lower; 156, top; 158, lower). These two publications appear in the bibliography under the name of their editor – Bianchi, Gabriella.

Two books, which are listed under Villoch in the bibliography, have recently been published by the Casa de las Ciencias in La Coruña. These describe, with admirable clarity, the species commonly sold in the Galician fish auctions. From them come the drawings on pages 30 (upper), 31, 42, 43, 82 (third), 129 (right), 131 (lower), 135 (lower), 137 (lower), 138 (all except bottom right), 148, and 149.

For the crustaceans I have leaned heavily on books by experts in that field: those of Professor Holthuis (136, upper); Dr Marit Christiansen (137, upper; 140); and Dr Adema (136, lower; 138, bottom right).

All the drawings of cephalopods, which appear on pages 162-6, excepting that of *Sepiola rondeleti,* come from the volume of *Danmarks Fauna,* cited under Muus in the bibliography, which deals with these creatures.

Drawings which I had previously used in my book *Mediterranean Seafood* (original sources acknowledged therein) are reproduced on pages 37, 90 (lower), 91, 99 (lower), 115, 144 (lower), 145 (upper), 146, 153, 154 (top), 158 (top), 161 (upper), 168 (upper), 169.

Similarly, drawings from my *North Atlantic Seafood* reappear on pages 143, 144 (upper), 147 (centre), 150 (lower), 161 (lower).

The artist Soun Vannithone, who has drawn scores of fish for me in the past, from the waters of his native S E Asia and also from the Atlantic and the Mediterranean, has on this occasion done new drawings which appear on the following pages: 19, 56, 141 (upper), 145 (lower), 156 (second and third), 157, 159, 160, 163 (*Sepiola rondeleti*), and 168 (the lower drawing, executed earlier for *A Kipper with My Tea*).

I have frequently had recourse in my work to the admirable three volumes on fish of the Mediterranean and the East Atlantic, prepared by a team of experts under the auspices of UNESCO (see under Whitehead in the bibliography). The numerous drawings in this work are described by the editors as coming from a variety of sources, some of which are no longer identifiable. Those which I have used, or adapted, are to be found on pages 58, 82 (second), 83, 84, 85 (lower), 89, 90 (upper), 113 (centre), 116, and 117. The drawings of the salmon and salmon trout on page 22 comes from Max Poll's splendid book on fish of Belgian waters.

INDEX

For a full list of our
essential books on Spain contact:
Santana Books,
Apartado 422,
29640 Fuengirola (Málaga) Spain.
Tel: 952 485 838. Fax 952 485 367.
E-mail: sales@santanabooks.com
www.santanabooks.com

UK Representatives
Aldington Books Ltd.,
Unit 3(b) Frith Business Centre,
Frith Road, Aldington,
Ashford, Kent TN25 7HJ.
Tel: 01233 720 123. Fax: 01233 721 272
E-mail: sales@aldingtonbooks.co.uk
www.aldingtonbooks.co.uk